Education
Language Arts

Grade 7: Module 1

The Lost Children of Sudan

Student Workbook
(Second Edition)

EL Education Language Arts Curriculum

Grade 7: Language Arts: Module 1: The Lost Children of Sudan, Student Workbook (Second Edition)

EL Education Language Arts Curriculum is published by:

EL Education

247 W. 35th Street, 8th Floor

New York, NY 10001

www.ELeducation.org

ISBN 978-1683626008

SECOND EDITION

Table of Contents

Grade 7: Module 1: The Lost Children of Sudan

Unit 3: Write to Raise Awareness: The Lost Children of South Sudan

Homework Resources

Affix List

About EL Education

"There is more in us than we know. If we can be made to see it, perhaps, for the rest of our lives, we will be unwilling to settle for less." – Kurt Hahn

EL Education is redefining student achievement in diverse communities across the country, ensuring that all students master rigorous content, develop positive character, and produce high-quality work. We create great public schools where they are needed most, inspiring teachers and students to achieve more than they thought possible.

EL Education's portfolio of instructional materials and coaching services draws on decades of deep partnership with schools and districts in our national school network—those implementing our school model—and in our family of literacy partners—those implementing our Language Arts curriculum.

Based on our founding principles of meaningful work, character, and respect for teachers, EL Education's offerings transform teaching and learning to promote habits of scholarship and character that lead to high student achievement. In addition to success on standardized tests, EL Education students demonstrate critical thinking, intellectual courage, and emotional resilience; they possess the passion and the capacity to contribute to a better world.

EL Education's curriculum is a comprehensive, standards-based core literacy program that engages teachers and students through compelling, real-world content by diverse authors. The curriculum has received the highest marks from EdReports.org and Educators Evaluating the Quality of Instructional Products (EQuIP). Rigorous impact studies by Mathematica Policy Research demonstrate that teachers significantly improve their craft and students achieve more, regardless of background.

EL Education, a 501c(3) nonprofit, was founded in 1992 by Outward Bound USA in collaboration with the Harvard Graduate School of Education. The ideas of Kurt Hahn, a founder of Outward Bound USA, have inspired and animated EL Education's work with schools since our founding. Hahn believed in the genius in every child, and in the power of education to help children develop academic courage and ethical character.

Unit 1

Entrance Ticket: Unit 1, Lesson 1

RI.7.1

Name: _____ **Date:**_____

Directions: As you enter class, read the following excerpt and answer the following prompts.

1. Read this learning target:

   I can use evidence to infer the topic of this module from the resources.

   Brainstorm ideas about the purpose of learning targets below.

   _____

   _____

   _____

Infer the Topic: I Notice/I Wonder
Note-Catcher

RL.7.1, RI.7.1

Name: _____ **Date:** _____

What do you think you will be learning about in this module?

I Notice (things I see)	I Wonder (questions I have)

Entrance Ticket: Unit 1, Lesson 2

L.7.4c

Name: _____ **Date:_____**

Directions: As you enter class, answer the following questions.

Read this learning target:

I can determine the difference between academic and domain-specific vocabulary.

Part A

What is **academic vocabulary**?

_____

_____

_____

_____

Part B

What is **domain-specific vocabulary**?

_____

_____

_____

_____

Academic and Domain-Specific Vocabulary Form

Name: _____ **Date:**_____

Academic Vocabulary: Words you might find in informational texts on many different topics. Draw a symbol, such as a star, next to academic vocabulary words.

Domain-Specific Vocabulary: Words about a particular topic, such as frogs.

Word and Pronunciation	Definition
What is the word and how do you say it? What is the translation in your home language?	What does it mean in your own words? * Add an optional sketch/diagram/icon.

Synopsis: *A Long Walk to Water*, Chapter 1

RL.7.2

Name: _____ **Date:** _____

- Tall, eleven-year-old Nya walks with a container in the heat.

- Eleven-year-old Salva is bored in school, listening to a lesson about the Arabic language.

- He is only able to attend school in the rainy season, as his family moves away during the dry season.

- His sisters do not go to school; they learn housework.

- The boys graze cattle, make cows out of clay, and practice with bows and arrows.

- Salva hears gunshots.

- Salva's teacher directs the students to run away into the bush.

- The gunshots are related to the war: the rebels in Southern Sudan were fighting against the government in Northern Sudan, over religion.

Entrance Ticket: Unit 1, Lesson 3

L.7.4a

Name: _____ **Date:**_____

Directions: As you enter class, answer the following questions.

Read this learning target:

I can identify strategies to answer selected response questions.

Part A

Use context to determine the meaning of the word **identify**.

_____

_____

Part B

Is this an academic or domain-specific vocabulary word?

_____

Which answer best defines the word **shapes** in the following learning target?

I can analyze how the setting shapes the characters and plot in chapters 1 and 2 of *A Long Walk to Water*.

A. to give a certain form or shape to; mold

B. an ordered or organized form

C. to give a direction or character to

D. physical condition

Synopsis: *A Long Walk to Water*, Chapter 2

RL.7.2

Name: _____ **Date:_____**

- Nya is jabbed in the foot by a thorn.
- Salva runs and walks for a long time.
- Other people are walking, too.
- They organize by village, but no one from his family is there.
- They arrive at the rebel camp, and the men are forced to go with the rebels.
- The women and children sleep in a barn that night.
- Salva is left all alone; the others walk on without him.

QuickWrite: Setting Shapes Character and Plot in *A Long Walk to Water*

RL.7.3

Name: _____ **Date:**_____

QuickWrite to answer this question (this means write whatever comes into your head based on what you have read in the text):

How does the setting shape the characters and plot in chapter 2 of *A Long Walk to Water*? Use text evidence to support your response.

Differentiated option: How does the setting shape the characters OR the plot in chapter 2 of *A Long Walk to Water*? Use text evidence to support your response.

_____

_____

_____

_____

_____

_____

_____

_____

_____

_____

_____

_____

_____

Notes

_____

_____

_____

_____

_____

_____

_____

_____

_____

Entrance Ticket: Unit 1, Lesson 4

L.7.4b

Name: _____ **Date:_____**

Directions: As you enter class, answer the following questions.

1. Read this learning target:

    I can identify strategies to determine the meaning of unfamiliar vocabulary.

    Part A

    Use context to determine the meaning of the word **determine**.

    _____

    _____

    Part B

    Is this an academic or domain-specific word?

    _____

2. Read the following quote from *A Long Walk to Water*:

    "Salva watched as one man protested that he did not want to go with the rebels."

    What is the root of the word **protested**? What does the root mean? What do the affixes mean? What is the origin of each part of the word? Use the affix list at your work space to break the word down into its affixes and root using this chart:

	Word Parts and Meaning	Origin
Prefix (before the root)		
Root		
Suffix (after the root)		

Synopsis: *A Long Walk to Water*, Chapter 3

RL.7.2

Name: _____ **Date:_____**

- Nya gets to the pond and fills her container.

- She begins the long walk home.

- Salva cries from loneliness.

- Salva stays with an old Dinka woman for a few days; Salva is from the Dinka tribe.

- The old Dinka woman asks him what he will do and where his family is, and he doesn't know.

- The old woman must leave to get away from the fighting and to find water.

- She tells Salva she must go alone as it is safer for her that way.

- Salva hears voices, and he leaves with other Dinka walkers.

Analyze Point of View:
A Long Walk to Water, Chapter 3

RL.7.1, RL.7.3, RL.7.6

Name: _____ **Date:**_____

Directions: Complete the following chart to answer the question: "How does Linda Sue Park contrast Nya's and Salva's points of view?"

What is Nya's point of view of arriving at the pond? How do you know? How has the author developed this point of view?

What is Salva's point of view of finding the old woman? How do you know? How has the author developed this point of view?

Tip:

What is a common feeling/emotion both Nya and Salva have? Some examples include fear, upset, anger, and relief.

Nya	Salva

How do you know? How has the author developed this point of view?	How do you know? How has the author developed this point of view?

Entrance Ticket: Unit 1, Lesson 5

RL.7.4

Name: _____ **Date:** _____

Directions: As you enter class, answer the following question.

Read this sentence from *A Long Walk to Water*:

"Salva **stumbled** back to the barn" (19).

What does the word **stumbled** tell you about how Salva is moving and how he is feeling?

_____

_____

_____

"The Lost Boys of the Sudan"

Name: _____ **Date:**_____

Since 1983, the Sudan People's Liberation Army (SPLA) and the Sudanese Government have been at war in southern Sudan. The conflict has already claimed more than 500,000 lives and displaced huge numbers of people. Among these were at least 20,000 children, mostly boys, between 7 and 17 years of age who were separated from their families. These 'lost boys' of the Sudan trekked enormous distances over a vast unforgiving wilderness, seeking refuge from the fighting. Hungry, frightened and weakened by sleeplessness and disease, they crossed from the Sudan into Ethiopia and back, with many dying along the way. The survivors are now in camps in Kenya, the Sudan and Uganda.

This extraordinary exodus has its origins in traditional forms of migration. After being initiated into manhood, young adolescent boys in southern Sudan have generally been quite mobile. Organized into small groups of their peers, they would leave home for a period to look after cattle. Or they might head for the towns or cities to go to school or to seek their fortune, before eventually returning home. In addition, at times of stress families all over Africa send their children elsewhere to find safety, food, work and schooling.

But during the war this process has escalated dramatically. Fearing they would be targeted as potential combatants, many boys left their villages and headed for cities such as Juba and Khartoum. Here they hoped to find work or schooling, though as these cities became saturated with migrants, the boys often had to resort to begging or petty crime.

Others set out for refugee camps in Ethiopia. Some travelled with friends or relatives, others slipped away on their own at night. Few had any idea of what lay ahead of them. They believed the trek would last only a few days and discovered that they faced a harrowing journey of 6 to 10 weeks. **Continually under threat, they would flee for their lives, losing their way in the wilderness**. Often they lost everything en route—blankets, sheets, shoes, clothes and pots—to soldiers, swindlers or bandits. Many fell victim to killer diseases. Others were so weakened by hunger and lack of sleep that they could go no further and sat down by the roadside—prey for lions and other animals.

The survivors who reached the camps in Ethiopia started to lead a relatively peaceful life. But it was not to last. Following the change of government in Ethiopia in May 1991 they had to flee again, back to camps in the Sudan. This time the journey was during heavy rains, and many perished crossing the swollen rivers or were hit by aerial bombardment. The luckier ones made it to a camp where they received help from the International Committee of the Red Cross.

This relative security was shattered again late in 1991 when fighting erupted around them, and they and children from other camps were on the move once more, eventually heading for Kenya.

Since 1992, UNICEF has managed to reunite nearly 1,200 boys with their families. But approximately 17,000 remain in camps in the region. The harsh memories remain as well. As 14-year-old Simon Majok puts it: "We were suffering because of war. Some have been killed. Some have died because of hunger and disease. We children of the Sudan, we were not lucky."

Source: "The Lost Boys of the Sudan." The State of the World's Children 1996. Copyright © 1996 UNICEF. Used by permission.

Close Read: "The Lost Boys of the Sudan" Note-Catcher

Name: _____ **Date:**_____

What are the central Ideas of this text? How does the author develop these ideas?

Source: "The Lost Boys of the Sudan." The State of the World's Children 1996. Copyright © 1996 UNICEF. Used by permission.

Paragraph 2
Main Idea: Supporting Details:

Paragraphs 3 and 4

Main Idea:

Hopes or Expectations:	Realities:

Other Supporting Details:

Central ideas of the article and how they are related:

Closing Paragraphs

How do these sentences and supporting details further develop the central ideas you identified?

Notes on the Final Sentence

Vocabulary

displaced (clues):

(definition):

harrowing (clues):

(definition):

Language Dive: "The Lost Boys of the Sudan," Paragraph 4 Note-Catcher

RL.7.1, RI.7.1

Name: _____ **Date:** _____

Continually under threat, they would flee for their lives, losing their way in the wilderness.

1. Create a complete sentence by filling in the boxes with an adjective phrase and a "would" clause.

Continually	I would

Sketch the Lost Boys "losing their way in the wilderness."

2. Complete the sentence frames to practice writing about a central theme in your own words:

Continually _____, the 'lost boys' would _____

_____, _____.

(adjective phrase + independent clause + gerund phrase)

QuickWrite: Make Connections

RL.7.1, RI.7.1

Name: _____ **Date:**_____

QuickWrite to answer this question (this means write whatever comes into your head based on what you have read in the text):

What connections are you making between "The Lost Boys of the Sudan" informational text, and *A Long Walk to Water*? What information is similar in both?

_____

_____

_____

_____

_____

_____

_____

_____

_____

_____

_____

_____

_____

_____

_____

_____

_____

Notes

_____

_____

_____

_____

_____

_____

_____

_____

_____

Entrance Ticket: Unit 1, Lesson 6

L.7.4c

Name: _____ **Date:** _____

Directions: As you enter class, answer the following question.

Read this sentence from *A Long Walk to Water*:

"The terrain changed from scrub to woodland; they walked among stands of **stunted** trees" (22–23).

Use a print or online dictionary, and copy the meaning of the word **stunted** as it is used in this sentence.

_____

_____

Synopsis: *A Long Walk to Water*, Chapter 4

RL.7.2

Name: _____ Date:_____

- Nya stops at home for a bowl of boiled sorghum meal and then returns to the pond with her little sister Akeer.

- Salva leaves the old woman's house.

- He joins a new group of people escaping, and they don't want to include him as he's another mouth to feed until a woman stands up for him.

- Unfortunately, no one from his family is with the group.

- Salva walks with a young man named Buksa, who leads the group to a beehive filled with honey.

Entrance Ticket: Unit 1, Lesson 7

L.7.4

Name: _____ **Date:** _____

Directions: As you enter class, answer the following question.

Read this sentence from *A Long Walk to Water*:

"Nothing had ever tasted so good as those pieces of honeycomb dripping with rich, **luscious** gold sweetness" (28).

From the context, what do you think **luscious** means? Write your first ideas below.

_____

_____

Now use a dictionary to check and correct your response in a different color.

Synopsis: *A Long Walk to Water*, Chapter 5

RL.7.2

Name: _____ **Date:** _____

- Nya's family moves to an area beside a lake.

- Nya's tribe, the Nuer, take a break from fighting their rival tribe, the Dinka, because both tribes are busy trying to survive the dry season.

- Nya must dig a hole and wait for water, for hours at a time.

- Salva meets a new friend named Marial.

- Salva and Marial walk together in lion-country and connect over their missing families.

Text-Dependent Questions:
A Long Walk to Water, Chapter 5

RL.7.1, RL.7.3, RL.7.4, RL.7.6, L.7.4

Name: _____ **Date:** _____

Read chapter 5 of *A Long Walk to Water*, then answer these questions.

1. Reread this excerpt from page 31: "He rubbed his eyes, rose, and **stumbled** after Marial as they began walking yet again."

    What meaning and tone does the word **stumbled** convey to the reader? (RL.7.4)

    A. Salva struggled to walk because he was so tired.

    B. Salva was ready to move on, so he got up enthusiastically.

    C. Salva was a very clumsy person.

    D. Salva was chasing Marial.

2. Reread this excerpt from page 26: ". . . when both tribes were so busy struggling for survival that the fighting **occurred** far less often."

    Use a print or online dictionary. Below, copy the meaning of the word **occurred** as it is used in this sentence. (L.7.4c, L.7.4d, L.7.6)

    _____

    _____

    _____

3. Reread this sentence from page 31: "Their region was **inhabited** by large herds of antelope, wildebeest, gnus—and the lions that preyed on them."

    Break this down into affixes and roots, and use your affix list to determine the meaning of the word **inhabited**. (L.7.4b)

	Affix	Meaning
Prefix		
Root		
Suffix		

Definition:

_____

_____

4. How does the setting shape the characters and plot in chapter 5 of *A Long Walk to Water*? Use details from the text to support your response. (RL.7.1, RL.7.3)

_____

_____

_____

_____

_____

_____

_____

_____

_____

_____

_____

_____

_____

5. Reread pages 30–31 from, "Do you know where we're going?" to ". . . their strides matching perfectly."

    What is Marial's point of view of the journey? How do you know? How has the author developed this point of view?

    What is Salva's point of view of finding the journey? How do you know? How has the author developed this point of view?

    How does Linda Sue Park develop and contrast the points of view of Marial and Salva about their journey? Use the chart to capture your thinking. (RL.7.1, RL.7.6)

    Tip: How do you know they feel different? How does Linda Sue Park help you understand that difference?

Marial's Point of View	Salva's Point of View
How do you know? How has the author developed this point of view?	How do you know? How has the author developed this point of view?
How does Linda Sue Park contrast Marial's and Salva's points of view?	

Entrance Ticket: Unit 1, Lesson 8

L.7.4

Name: _____ **Date:**_____

Directions: As you enter class, answer the following question.

Read this sentence from chapter 5 of *A Long Walk to Water*:

"Their region was inhabited by large herds of **antelope**, **wildebeest**, **gnus**—and the lions that preyed on them" (31).

Use context to determine the meanings of the words **antelope**, **wildebeest**, and **gnus**. Write your ideas on the lines below.

_____

_____

_____

Check your definitions in the dictionary, make any corrections to your definitions, and draw pictures of the words below.

Synopsis: *A Long Walk to Water*, Chapter 6

RL.7.2

Name: _____ **Date:** _____

- Nya likes the lake because there is no long walk to water.

- Nya's mother hates the lake because they do not have a house and her husband and her son are in danger.

- Salva's uncle is in the group.

- Salva's uncle shoots an antelope, but because they haven't eaten in such a long time, they all get sick.

- Marial is missing, probably because a lion attacked him.

Chapter 6 Synopsis

Chapter 6 of *A Long Walk to Water* shows Nya and Salva struggling to survive dangerous environments. Both of their families help them, but sometimes this is not enough. Nya and her family have moved to a lake camp where life is difficult. Nya struggles to get water. She also realizes that her mother is afraid that the men in the family will become involved in the fighting near the camp. This shows how her mother is protective of the family. In Salva's section, the struggle to survive continues. Salva's uncle shoots an antelope for the group to eat. It is their first real meal in a long time, so they all get sick. The group wanders a long time looking for water before going to sleep. When Salva wakes, his uncle tells him he has some bad news about his friend. Nya's and Salva's struggles show that even when people work together, nature can be overpowering.

Entrance Ticket: Unit 1, Lesson 9

L.7.4

Name: _____ **Date:** _____

Directions: As you enter class, answer the following question.

Read the learning targets:

I can identify themes in *A Long Walk to Water* and how they have developed over the course of the text.

I can identify the characteristics of an effective synopsis.

Use context to determine the meaning of the phrase **over the course of**. Write your definition on the lines below.

_____

_____

Is this an academic or domain-specific phrase? How do you know?

_____

_____

Have you seen it elsewhere? If so, where?

_____

_____

Synopsis: *A Long Walk to Water*, Chapter 7

RL.7.2

Name: _____ **Date:** _____

- Akeer is dangerously ill with a bad stomachache, fever, cramps, and diarrhea that can kill children and the elderly.

- Nya's family struggles with the decision of whether or not to travel with Akeer on the long three-day walk to clinic.

- While sleeping, Marial was killed by a lion, leaving only a few splotches of blood as evidence.

- Salva's uncle calms and reassures Salva about the lions.

- Soon they reach the Nile river and weave together reeds to make shallow canoes to cross it.

- After that, they'll head through the desert and on to Ethiopia.

Common Themes in Literature

RL.7.2

Name: _____ **Date:** _____

What is **theme**?

The **theme** of a book is the message or main idea relevant to the real world that the author wants the reader to take away from reading a literary text.

A theme has the following characteristics:

- It is a message or lesson about life that is broadly applicable—it can be true for situations beyond the story.

- It is a statement, not just a topic. That is, "friendship" is not a theme. However, "Friendship can bring comfort in times of hardship" could be a theme.

- Different books or movies can have similar themes. For example, the stories "Little Red Riding Hood" and "Hansel and Gretel" both convey the message that you should be careful about whom you trust, because people may not share their true intentions. The plots of these fairy tales are quite different, but their themes are similar.

Directions

Read through the list of some common themes in literature with your partner. Choose three that might be themes in *A Long Walk to Water*. Be prepared to explain why you selected each one.

1. Nature can present many challenges to humans.

2. Family is our most important support.

3. Love is what makes life worth living.

4. Dangerous situations can make people become leaders.

5. To be truly happy, you must do what you know is right, even if it is unpopular.

6. Individuals are able to survive in challenging environments in remarkable ways.

7. People need to depend on one another in order to survive.

8. In challenging situations, it can be helpful to focus only on small steps.

Model Summary: *A Long Walk to Water*, Chapter 6

RL.7.3

Name: _____ **Date:** _____

Write a brief summary of chapter 6 of *A Long Walk to Water*.

Chapter 6 of *A Long Walk to Water* shows Nya and Salva struggling to survive dangerous environments. Both of their families help them, but sometimes this is not enough. Nya and her family have moved to a lake camp where life is difficult. Nya struggles to get water. She also realizes that her mother is afraid that the men in the family will become involved in the fighting near the camp. This shows how her mother is protective of the family. In Salva's section, the struggle to survive continues. Salva's uncle shoots an antelope for the group to eat. It is their first real meal in a long time, so it makes them sick. The group wanders a long time looking for water before going to sleep. When Salva wakes, his uncle tells him he has some bad news about his friend. Nya's and Salva's struggles show that even when people work together, nature can be overpowering.

introduces the text by stating the title and chapter; clearly states the author's central idea

objective

includes the most important details from the text to show support of the central ideas and themes

concise

concludes with a theme

Notes

_____

_____

_____

_____

_____

_____

_____

_____

_____

_____

_____

_____

_____

_____

_____

_____

_____

Entrance Ticket: Unit 1, Lesson 10

L.7.2a

Name: _____ Date:_____

Directions: As you enter class, respond to the following prompt.

Read the following sentence taken from chapter 7 in *A Long Walk to Water*:

"He clung to Uncle like a baby or a little boy hanging on to hand or shirttail

whenever he could never letting Uncle get farther than an arm's length away."

(40)

Punctuate the sentence correctly.

Language Dive: *A Long Walk to Water*, Page 44 Note-Catcher

RL.7.2, L.7.1a

Name: _____ **Date:** _____

Every time Salva delivered a load of reeds, **he would pause for a few moments** to admire the skills of the boat-builders.

1. Create a complete sentence by filling in the boxes with an adverbial phrase and a "would" clause.

Every time I	I would

2. Complete the following sentence frame to mirror the original sentence from *A Long Walk to Water*:

Every time I _____,
past tense verb

I would _____

to _____.
infinitive phrase

Sketch Salva carrying a load of reeds or admiring the skills of the boat-builders.

Themes and Summary:
A Long Walk to Water, Chapter 7

RL.7.1, RL.7.2

Name: _____ **Date:**_____

Part I

How has the author developed a theme?

Directions: Identify a theme you have seen represented multiple times in the book so far. Collect evidence of that theme on the note-catcher below.

Theme: _____

Evidence of Theme (provide chapter)	How has the author developed the theme from the time it was evident? How has the way the theme has been conveyed changed from the last example?

Evidence of Theme (provide chapter)	How has the author developed the theme from the time it was evident? How has the way the theme has been conveyed changed from the last example?

Part II

Directions: Answer the following questions to help you draft a brief summary of chapter 7.

1. Underline the three most important details that should be included in a summary of this chapter.

   A. Nya thinks of others with the same disease as her sister.

   B. Akeer's illness is getting worse.

   C. Salva hangs on to his uncle's shirt when he can.

   D. Salva is upset and scared because his friend Marial is gone.

   E. Salva's group works together to build canoes to get across the river.

   F. Salva's uncle jokes with him about not bringing a boat.

2. (Thinking about thinking) How did you decide which three details to choose? Which ones link to the theme you selected? How?

   _____

   _____

   _____

3. Using the criteria you helped to generate from the previous lesson as a guide, write a rough draft of a brief summary of this chapter in the space below.

_____

_____

_____

_____

_____

_____

_____

_____

_____

_____

_____

_____

_____

_____

_____

All quotations in this handout from:
Park, Linda Sue. *A Long Walk to Water: Based on a True Story*. Houghton Mifflin Harcourt, 2010. Chapter 7.

Entrance Ticket: Unit 1, Lesson 11

L.7.2a

Name: _____ **Date:** _____

Directions: As you enter class, answer the following question.

Which of these shows the correct punctuation of a sentence from chapter 8 of *A Long Walk to Water*?

- A. Those he could reach, though he scratched until they bled.
- B. Those he could reach though he scratched, until they bled.
- C. Those, he could reach though he scratched until they bled.
- D. Those he could reach, though, he scratched until they bled.

Themes and Summary:
A Long Walk to Water, Chapter 8

RL.7.1, RL.7.2

Name: _____ **Date:** _____

Directions: Answer the following questions in order to help you draft a brief summary of chapter 8.

1. What is happening to Akeer in the beginning of the chapter? Why? Cite examples from the text.

   _____

   _____

   _____

   _____

   _____

2. Why was coming upon the fishermen significant for Salva's group? Underline one answer.

   A. They learn about fishing.

   B. They are able to get food.

   C. They get new information about the war.

   D. They learn how to protect themselves from mosquitoes.

3. What can you infer from the last two paragraphs of the chapter (page 50)? Underline two answers.

   A. That many of the travelers have been to the Akobo desert.

   B. That the travelers were beginning to fight with one another.

   C. That the travelers wanted to bring the fishermen with them.

   D. That there won't be much water where the travelers are going.

   E. That the travelers are concerned about the next part of their journey.

4. Using the criteria you helped to generate from previous lessons as a guide, write a rough draft of a brief summary of this chapter in the space below.

_____

_____

_____

_____

_____

_____

_____

_____

_____

_____

_____

_____

_____

_____

_____

_____

All quotations in this handout from:
Park, Linda Sue. *A Long Walk to Water: Based on a True Story*. Houghton Mifflin Harcourt, 2010. Chapter 8.

Entrance Ticket: Unit 1, Lesson 12

Name: _____ **Date:**_____

Directions: As you enter class, answer the following questions.

Review the feedback on your Mid-Unit 1 Assessment.

Based on your work in the Mid-Unit 1 Assessment, what is one star (area of strength) you want to continue to show in today's assessment?

_____

_____

_____

What is one step (area of growth) you want to improve in today's assessment?

_____

_____

_____

If you would like support to understand the feedback, please write your names on the board for a one-on-one review.

Entrance Ticket: Unit 1, Lesson 13

SL.7.1

Name: _____ Date:_____

Directions: As you enter class, answer the following questions.

What are some words or phrases you can say to hear more about what your partner or group member is saying in a discussion?

_____

_____

_____

_____

_____

What are some words or phrases that stop the discussion?

_____

_____

_____

_____

_____

Synopsis: *A Long Walk to Water*, Chapter 10

RL.7.2

Name: _____ **Date:**_____

- The strangers say that they will find water in between two trees.

- Nya is in disbelief that this is possible.

- Salva wants to give water to the dying travelers, but his uncle says that he isn't strong enough.

- Three women give water to the dying, and they are revived.

- They join the group.

- Salva worries how his parents will find him.

- Salva's uncle suspects that Salva's family is dead, as his village of Loun-Ariik was attacked and probably burned.

- They are one day from the refugee camp.

- After taking Salva to the camp, his uncle will return to Sudan to fight in the war.

- No one in the group has eaten anything for two days, and their water is nearly gone.

- Six men from the Nuer tribe armed with guns and machetes loot the group and take Salva's uncle's gun.

- Then, the soldiers kill Salva's uncle.

Themes: *A Long Walk to Water*, Chapter 10

RL.7.1, RL.7.2

Name: _____ Date: _____

How has the author developed a theme?

Directions: Identify a theme from chapter 10 you have seen represented multiple times in the book so far. Collect evidence of that theme on the note-catcher below.

Theme: _____

Evidence of Theme (provide chapter)	How has the author developed the theme from the time it was evident? How has the way the theme has been conveyed changed from the last example?

Evidence of Theme (provide chapter)	How has the author developed the theme from the time it was evident? How has the way the theme has been conveyed changed from the last example?

Entrance Ticket: Unit 1, Lesson 14

W.7.8

Name: _____ **Date:** _____

Directions: As you enter class, answer the following question.

Read the following sentence.

Linda Sue Park shows the group's collaboration when she writes, "Immediately, the group began making preparations to cook and eat the bird" (61).

This is a quote from *A Long Walk to Water*. Looking at this model, what are two criteria you might generate for quoting accurately from the text?

_____

_____

_____

_____

Synopsis: *A Long Walk to Water*, Chapter 11

RL.7.2

Name: _____ **Date:**_____

- The men and the village clear the land, which is dangerous because there are scorpions and poisonous snakes.

- Nya is puzzled and doubtful that there is water in the dry ground.

- Salva feels sad, but also feels that Marial and his uncle have left him with strength to help him on his journey.

- Without his uncle in the group, Salva now has to beg for scraps, even though his uncle had been generous with everyone.

- At the refugee camp at Itang, Salva was separated from the group, and he felt frightened.

- Salva looks for his family at the crowded camp.

- After such a long time walking, it felt strange to Salve to sit still, and he felt restless.

- Salva is finally able to eat at the camp: he's given a bowl of boiled maize each morning.

- Salva thinks he sees his tall mother in the crowd, with her orange headscarf.

Prepare for a Text-Based Discussion: Themes: *A Long Walk to Water* Note-Catcher

RL.7.1, RL.7.2, SL.7.1

Name: _____ Date:_____

Question: How do Salva and Nya overcome adversity? What theme might the author be developing through these characters?

Themes	Evidence/Example from the Text	Elaboration (How does this evidence support the theme?)

Quote Accurately from the Text

RL.7.1, RI.7.1

Name: _____ **Date:**_____

Sometimes in writing, you will need to include a direct quote from a text.

When quoting from a text:

- Copy the exact words that are in the text.

- Give the page number that the quote is from.

  - If the page number is not in the sentence, then put it after the quote in parentheses: "Quote" (75).

  - If you quote more than one author, use the authors' names in parentheses with the page number: "Quote" (Park 75).

- Use quotation marks ("quote") to show the words that have come word for word from the text.

- If using "he said," "she said," or "it says," for example, put a comma before the quotation marks. (On page 30 Miguel said, "Quote.")

Entrance Ticket: Unit 1, Lessons 15–16

SL.7.1

Name: _____ **Date:_____**

Directions: As you enter class, answer the following questions.

1. Read the Discussion Norms anchor chart.

    Part A
    Which of the norms do you think you might find challenging today?

    _____

    _____

    Part B
    What can you do to overcome this challenge?

    _____

    _____

    Part C
    What will help you to feel you can succeed at this discussion?

    _____

    _____

    _____

2. What value does today's discussion assessment have for you?

    _____

    _____

    _____

    _____

3. What does this discussion assessment mean to you beyond the work you are doing in the classroom?

_____

_____

_____

_____

Peer Critique Note-Catcher

SL.7.1

Name: _____ **Date:**_____

Directions: Record a peer's name on the lines provided when you observe someone demonstrating the discussion norms or cues. If you are observing only one peer, record the peer's name on the line below and place check or tally marks when you observe your peer demonstrating the discussion norms or cues.

Peer's Name: _____

Criteria Checklist

_____ listens carefully and waits turn to speak (does not interrupt).

_____ asks questions to better understand what people are saying.

_____ makes comments that contribute to the discussion.

_____ uses evidence to support ideas.

_____ responds to questions to help people better understand what they are saying and to build on the discussion.

_____ stays on topic.

_____ links ideas to those of others.

_____ speaks in complete sentences.

_____ assumes positive intent.

Cues
Expand a Response
 • "Can you say more about that?" _____ • "Can you give an example?" _____ • "I'm interested in what you said about . . . Can you tell me more?" _____ _____ • "Can you give us more details about . . . ?" _____ • "How did you come to that conclusion? What made you think that?" _____ _____ • "What did you learn/do you hope to learn from . . . ? Why?" _____ _____
Clarify a Response
 • "So, do you mean . . .?" _____ • "I'm not sure I understand . . . Can you clarify?" _____ • "Could you say that again? I'm not sure I understand." _____

Track Progress: Collaborative Discussion

Name: _____ **Date:** _____

Learning Target: I can participate in an effective collaborative discussion.

Standards I'm Tracking: SL.7.1

1. How am I doing?

    – For each criterion, self-assess by putting a check mark in the appropriate column.

    – Strive to be honest with yourself. Remember, your ability grows with your effort, so it's fine if you aren't there yet!

You will receive feedback on different-colored sticky notes/flags and in a different-colored pen on the checklist.

Standard	Characteristics of an Effective Collaborative Discussion	4 Advanced	3 Proficient	2 Developing	1 Beginning
SL.7.1a	I prepared for the discussion by reading and/or finding appropriate evidence in the text(s).				
SL.7.1b	I set specific goals for discussion.				
SL.7.1a	I use the evidence I prepared to support my ideas during the discussion.				
SL.7.1b	I follow agreed-upon rules for the discussion.				
SL.7.1b	I carry out the role I have been given in a discussion.				
SL.7.1c	I ask for more detail about others' ideas.				

Standard	Characteristics of an Effective Collaborative Discussion	4 Advanced	3 Proficient	2 Developing	1 Beginning
SL.7.1d	When needed, I use questions and comments to bring the discussion back on topic.				
SL.7.1d	I consider new ideas carefully and, when warranted, change my thinking.				

2. How have I improved since I last worked on this skill?

_____

_____

_____

Teacher Response:

_____

_____

_____

3. How can I improve next time?

_____

_____

_____

Teacher Response:

_____

_____

_____

Anchor Standard

SL.1

By the end of Grade 12 I will be able to: prepare for and participate effectively in a range of conversations and collaborations with diverse partners, building on others' ideas and expressing my own clearly and persuasively.

Unit 2

Entrance Ticket: Unit 2, Lesson 1

RI.7.1

Name: _____ **Date:**_____

Directions: As you enter class, answer the following question.

Read the following title of an article: "The 'Lost Girls' of Sudan."

Which questions from the Questions about *A Long Walk to Water* anchor chart do you think this article will answer?

_____

_____

_____

_____

_____

"The 'Lost Girls' of Sudan" by Ishbel Matheson

Name: _____ **Date:**_____

Just before the entrance of Kakuma refugee camp in the desert of Northern Kenya, a billboard proclaims "Women rights are human rights."

But across the barrier, in the hot, teeming warren of huts and dust roads, 17-year-old Grace Anyieth has not seen much evidence of this slogan being put into practice.

In her foster mother's compound, she picks through beans, sifting out dirt, preparing lunch.

She lists her chores: cooking, cleaning, washing, fetching water from the distant stand-pipe, looking after her guardian's children.

In other words, she is an unpaid servant.

Grace and thousands of other Sudanese children—most of them boys—staggered out of their war-torn homeland to Kenya in 1992.

They had an extraordinary story to tell.

After their parents had been killed or lost in the mayhem of the civil war in Southern Sudan, the children spent years wandering through conflict and famine, dodging armies, militias and animal predators, seeking a place of safety.

New Start

It was an epic march, which captured the attention of the world.

But while many of the boys—who became known as the "Lost Boys"—were resettled in the United States, the girls' claim for equal treatment was overlooked.

"Why not the girls?" Grace asks, "I would have liked the chance to go abroad. You can be free there. Free to work, free to study."

Few have thought to inquire about the fate of the "Lost Girls".

Although an estimated 3,000 arrived in Kakuma in 1992, most have simply vanished from official records.

We find Ayen at school in Kakuma, listening to a lesson on human rights.

A tall, striking, young woman, Ayen would like to continue with her education.

But at 18, she feels time is running out.

"The problem is that my foster-parents could find a rich man, and then they will marry me off. Even if I don't want to go, they will insist."

The boys and girls were separated as soon as they arrived in Kakuma in 1992.

Valuable Brides

The boys were kept together as a group, living in villages within the camp.

According to Sudanese custom, the girls were placed with guardians who were supposed to protect them.

But many foster-parents—it seems—did not have the girls' welfare at heart.

In a place where poverty is rampant, young women are a valuable commodity.

They can be sold off for a good bride-price.

When international attention focused on the lost boys, the Sudanese community kept the girls away from the limelight.

Sudanese leader, Gideon Kenyi, says, "The issue of dowries had become a priority to the people who are owning the girls. They see the girls as a way of generating wealth, by marrying them or by giving them to someone rich."

Refugee workers from international agencies assumed that the girls were safe, because they were being sheltered by their own people.

That assumption has turned out to be wide of the mark. But the head of the UN refugee agency in Kakuma, Kofi Mable, is doubtful that the girls can be helped now.

Living in Fear

Most no longer meet the strict resettlement criteria demanded by host countries, for single, unaccompanied minors.

"We have lost them . . . they are completely lost," Mr. Mable says regretfully, "They have lost that status of lost girls. Some of them are mothers. They are married . . . There's nothing I can do—or anyone else can do."

But it is clear that some of the 'Lost Girls' continue to suffer greatly.

Source: Matheson, Ishbel. "The 'Lost Girls' of Sudan." *BBC News*, 7 June 02. Used under BBC terms for not for profit use.

Close Read: "The 'Lost Girls' of Sudan" Note-Catcher

RI.7.1, RI.7.2, RI.7.4, L.7.4

Name: _____ **Date:** _____

Central Idea 1:	Central Idea 2:
Supporting Details:	Supporting Details:

Summary: Write a summary of the article. In your summary, be sure to identify the two central ideas and the details the author uses to develop these central ideas.

_____

_____

_____

_____

_____

_____

_____

_____

_____

_____

_____

_____

_____

_____

_____

_____

_____

_____

_____

_____

Language Dive: "The 'Lost Girls' of Sudan," Paragraph 10 Note-Catcher

RI.7.2, W.7.2c

Name: _____ **Date:** _____

But **while many of the boys**—who became known as the 'Lost Boys'—were resettled in the United States, the girls' claim for equal treatment was overlooked.

1. Create a complete sentence by filling in the first box with a word that makes the two phrases contrast each other.

	I like learning,	I get sad about some of the things I learn about.

2. Complete the following sentence frame to talk about how Nya and Salva, the two main characters in the novel *A Long Walk to Water*, were from different tribes.

    But while Nya—who was born after the war—is from the Nuer tribe,

    Salva _____.

Sketch or draw a diagram showing how what happened to the "Lost Girls" and the "Lost Boys" was different.

Make Connections Note-Catcher

RL.7.9

Name: _____

Date: _____

Directions: Use this note-catcher to keep track of connections between the informational texts in the unit and the novel *A Long Walk to Water*.

Informational Text	Idea or Text Excerpt from Informational Text	How Does It Connect?	Text from *A Long Walk to Water*

Informational Text	Idea or Text Excerpt from Informational Text	How Does It Connect?	Text from *A Long Walk to Water*

Entrance Ticket: Unit 2, Lesson 2

SL.7.2

Name: _____ **Date:** _____

Directions: As you enter class, answer the following questions.

Read the following learning target:

I can analyze the main ideas and supporting details in a clip from *God Grew Tired of Us.*

What if any are the differences between main ideas and central ideas?

_____

_____

_____

_____

What other questions do you have about this learning target?

_____

_____

_____

_____

Synopsis: *A Long Walk to Water*, Chapter 13

RL.7.2

Name: _____ **Date:** _____

- The crew struggles with supplying water to the borehole to keep the drill running, but their boss keeps them working.

- The soldiers force the refugees into the crocodile-infested river.

- Salva jumps in and a small boy grabs him by the neck and pushes him under the water.

- Soldiers shoot the boy, but Salva survives.

- Salva swims for what feels like years and finally makes it, exhausted, to the other side.

- At least 1,000 people died trying to cross the river.

- Salva becomes the leader of 1,500 boys as they walk through war-torn Sudan under the protection of night.

- They hide during the day, on their long walk to Kenya.

- They divided up jobs, shared food, and Salva led with his family at the forefront of his mind.

- He offered the boys the same encouragement that his uncle had offered him.

- It took them a year and a half for more than 1,200 boys to safely arrive in Kenya.

Main Ideas and Supporting Details: *God Grew Tired of Us* (11:07–13:30) Note-Catcher

SL.7.2

Name: _____ **Date:_____**

Use this chart to analyze the main ideas and supporting details in this clip of *God Grew Tired of Us*. Use the box labeled "Common elements in a video" as a reference for your analysis.

Common elements in a video (for reference): specific images, video, maps, graphics, narration, interviews, music
Main Ideas from the Video
Supporting Details

Brief Summary

_____

_____

_____

_____

_____

_____

_____

_____

_____

_____

_____

_____

_____

_____

_____

_____

_____

_____

Entrance Ticket: Unit 2, Lesson 3

W.7.7, L.7.4

Name: _____ **Date:**_____

Directions: As you enter class, answer the following questions.

Read this learning target:

I can research to answer questions about the Lost Children of Sudan.

Use context and word parts to determine the meaning of the word **research**.

_____

_____

_____

Is this an academic or domain-specific word?

_____

_____

Have you seen it elsewhere?

_____

_____

Choose and Use Credible Internet Sources

W.7.8

Name: _____ **Date:** _____

You can determine whether an internet source is reliable by identifying the publisher, author, bias, accuracy, and timeliness of the source.

- **Publisher:** A reliable internet source is usually published by the government (.gov), educational institutions (.edu), or nonprofit organizations (.org). Sometimes internet sources published by commercial organizations (.com) are reliable, but not always.

- **Author:** You can tell whether an internet source is accurate by looking at who wrote it and checking the writer's credentials.

- **Bias:** An internet source that presents both sides of an argument or does not have any bias and that presents facts is also usually reliable.

- **Accuracy:** A reliable internet source should be visually appealing, clean, and uncluttered, with links that work. It should not have many errors in spelling or grammar.

- **Timeliness:** An internet source that is reliable is timely; it does not have out-of-date information.

"One Day I Had to Run"
by John Deng Langbany

Name: _____ **Date:**_____

My first memories of my childhood start when I was about five years old in my homeland of Sudan, the day when my parents' house was burned. It was the last day I saw them. I ran with thousands of other young children in a very hard journey we made it across the desert all the way to Ethiopia. I was small so the other children carried me there. I have many memories of my time in Ethiopia. I survived through the worst sort of life that I'd ever seen. Every day people were dying. I was living with a group of children in Panyido, Ethiopia who had also lost their families. In Panyido, I couldn't do a lot of the things that the other children did because I was the youngest. For example, when they swam in the river I couldn't do it because the crocodiles would pick on me. I had to be scared all the time. I was good at climbing trees, but not at swimming. One day I decided to cross the river with a few of my friends who carried me across so we could get to a tree to catch some mongoose. Somebody came with a gun and he shot at us in the tree. He was an Ethiopian who hated us. We all had to jump down. We fell into the river. When I jumped into the river, I went too deep and my stomach was bleeding and I couldn't breathe. I thought I would be someone who wouldn't live anymore. It was painful. One of my friends was killed and one kid drowned in the water. They never found his body. I lived.

In 1991, when the government of Ethiopia fell apart, the new government chased us out of Panyido. We were chased to the edge of a big river that ran very fast, called Gillo. They kept shooting at us, so either you jumped in the water and they knew that you would drown because the water was way too fast or you would be shot. I didn't know how to swim so all day I watched people being killed. There was a lot of crying. The people crossing the river had to throw all their bags away but it didn't do any good because the shooting continued. I was crying as people near me were being shot. The river was full of people. You realized later they were all dead. I needed to get across the river. I was thinking all day what I could do about it. I knew there was no one to help me. It seemed like forever. I was too little and I didn't have parents to help me cross the river and I didn't know whether my brother had already made it across or not or where he was. I remembered how the elders had shown us how to protect ourselves, so I covered myself with a person who was dead. When the shooting cooled down, I asked the boy next to me if he would try to cross the river with me. He didn't know how to swim either. I threw myself in. I don't know how, but the river was moving so fast it brought me to the other side. That's how I crossed the river that killed so many people.

I followed the other children who survived to a place called Pachala. It took three days walking by foot. We didn't have water or anything. Pachala was on the Sudan side of the border with Ethiopia. When we got there, we saw hunger like I'd never seen in my life. There was no UN, no nothing. If you found one kernel of corn you lived off that for a day or two. Water and a little corn. It was a tough life. We lived like that for two months. Then the UNHCR came in and started bringing food. Just as things got a little better with food, the enemy from Ethiopia crossed the border and the fighting began again. We had to leave Pachala. Before I could leave, one of the ladies told me to wait while everyone left so they could see if I could be carried out in a Red Cross car for the injured and the smallest children, so I stayed behind.

A month after the rest of the kids had left, I was playing in the little river with the other children and the enemy came. While I was jumping in the water, I heard a sound. It was a bullet, but I didn't know what it was. When I got out of the water, the kids I was playing with were gone. I couldn't run because the bullets were all around me. I stayed flat and waited until nighttime. It was dark. I escaped from the river to the airstrip. There was also shooting at the airstrip. I stayed down. I tried to go to my house. I didn't know that the people who were living with me were all gone. When I got to my house, I accidentally kicked a can and the enemy heard me. They captured me. They took me to the place where they had a lot of people they'd captured. I stayed there for most of the night. Sometime before morning hours, I escaped under the fence.

I walked all the way to Oboth. On my way, I found one of my friends dead on the road. I had lived with him. His name was Mabil. It took me a long time to get to Oboth. On the way, there was a lot of shelling on the road. I thank God I was not killed. The shells missed me. When I got to Oboth, I met with the Sudanese people. I walked for three days to get to a place called Okila. I found the Sudanese Red Cross lady that had told me not to leave Pachala. She was still alive. I was happy. From there, we went to a place called Buma. In Buma, I found the UN and they announced that they would take the little children. At night, we were trying to sleep but some people came and shot at us. Three of my friends were killed. One was my father's brother-in-law. He was sleeping in the same bed as my brother, but my brother Aleer Gideon did not get shot. I ran into a tent but I didn't know there was a cooking fire inside. I threw myself in the fire to escape the shooting. I was burned. In the morning, after we got shot at, we left Magose to go to Kapoeta. We didn't stop there. We were with Red Cross vehicles and we went all the way to Nairus. We stayed there. There was no food for a while. The UN had to come in and give us food.

While we were in Nairus, the enemy captured Kapoeta again so the UN decided to bring us to Lokichiogio across the border into Kenya. When we came to Lokichiogio, we lived there but were still scared that something might happen again so the UN decided to bring us Kakuma, Kenya further in from the border. This was in 1992. In Kakuma, the native people treated us badly because they didn't know us. They were nomadic people called Turkana. They didn't know Sudanese. In 1994, I went back to Sudan. In 1995, I went to Ifo in Kenya. I lived in a refugee camp there trying to find a way to get to America. Three years later, I flew out of Nairobi to America and started high school in Rochester, Minnesota. I didn't know if I would find a good way of living anymore before I came to

America. When I graduated from high school, I started community college and now I'll be going to Winona State University.

It took me a long time to realize that I have gained a lot from living with so many people in the refugee camps. Nobody can believe it that I can speak 14 different languages. It was a part of learning while going through bad things. You can go through a lot but one day things can change. With my classmates, I don't compare myself to them. I didn't have a good life when I was a young kid, but today I've learned more and I have a good life. This is a summary of my experiences but there is more to explain for each example I've given. I'm so glad I'm still alive and this is my story.

Source: Excerpted from Wilkes, Sybella (Ed.). *One Day We Had to Run!: Refugee Children Tell Their Stories in Words and Paintings*. Millbrook Press, 1994. Used by permission of the editor. All rights reserved.

Entrance Ticket: Unit 2, Lesson 4

L.7.4d

Name: _____ **Date:**_____

Directions: As you enter class, respond to the following prompts.

Read these learning targets:

I can determine the central ideas in an informational text and analyze their development over the course of the text.

I can write an objective summary of an informational text.

Test yourself on the meanings of the words **central**, **analyze**, **development**, **over the course**, and **objective** by writing their meanings below and then checking the definitions in your vocabulary log.

central: _____

analyze: _____

development: _____

over the course: _____

objective: _____

Entrance Ticket: Unit 2, Lessons 5–6

SL.7.2

Name: _____ **Date:** _____

Directions: As you enter class, respond to the following prompts.

Read this learning target:

I can analyze the main ideas and supporting details in a clip from *God Grew Tired of Us.*

Recall the last time you watched a clip of this documentary in a previous lesson. What do you remember about the video? What questions did it help to answer for you?

_____

_____

_____

_____

_____

_____

Synopsis: *A Long Walk to Water*, Chapter 14

RL.7.2

Name: _____ **Date:** _____

- After three days of drilling, suddenly water sprays out of the hole but is dirty.
- Salva is now 22 years old.
- He was in the Kakuma refugee camp for two years, which was a terrible place, dry and prison-like.
- Salva and a few other young men walk for months to Ifo, another refugee camp.
- It is no better there.
- Michael, an aide worker, teaches Salva how to speak and read English and how to play volleyball.
- A rumor spreads that young men were being chosen from the camp to go to America.
- Each time a list is posted, Salva gets anxious, but his name isn't on the list.
- One day, Michael tells Salva that his name is on the list.
- Salva will go to Rochester, New York.

Track Progress: Research

Name: _____ **Date:** _____

Learning Target: I can gather information through research to build knowledge and answer research questions.

Standards I'm Tracking: W.7.7 and W.7.8

1. How am I doing?

    – For each criterion, self-assess by putting a check mark in the appropriate column.

    – Write the number of each standard on a sticky note or flag. Then on your own writing, place each sticky note in an area that shows evidence you have met that criterion. Make sure you have evidence for each criterion.

    – Strive to be honest with yourself. Remember, your ability grows with your effort, so it's fine if you aren't there yet!

You will receive feedback on different-colored sticky notes/flags and in a different-colored pen on the checklist

Standard	Characteristics of Effective Research	4 Advanced	3 Proficient	2 Developing	1 Beginning
W.7.7	I can use several sources to answer a research question.				
W.7.7	I can generate additional, related, focused questions to support my investigation.				
W.7.8	I can use search terms effectively.				
W.7.8	I can gather relevant information from several print and digital sources, and take organized notes.				

Standard	Characteristics of Effective Research	4 Advanced	3 Proficient	2 Developing	1 Beginning
W.7.8	I can assess the credibility and accuracy of each source.				
W.7.8	I can quote or paraphrase information and ideas from research without plagiarizing.				
W.7.8	I can cite sources using a standard format.				

2. How have I improved since I last worked on this skill?

_____

_____

_____

Teacher Response:

_____

_____

_____

3. How can I improve next time?

_____

_____

_____

Teacher Response:

_____

_____

_____

Anchor Standards

W.7

By the end of Grade 12 I will be able to: conduct short as well as more sustained research projects based on focused questions, demonstrating understanding of the subject under investigation.

W.8

By the end of Grade 12 I will be able to: gather relevant information from multiple print and digital sources, assess the credibility and accuracy of each source, and integrate the information while avoiding plagiarism.

Entrance Ticket: Unit 2, Lesson 7

RI.7.1

Name: _____ **Date:**_____

Directions: As you enter class, respond to the following prompts.

Read the following learning target:

I can use the Painted Essay® structure to analyze a model.

If you are familiar with the Painted Essay®, what is it? If you are not familiar with the Painted Essay®, what do you think it is based on the context of the learning target?

_____

_____

_____

_____

_____

_____

Compare and Contrast Model Essay

RL.7.9, W.7.2

Name: _____ Date:_____

How has the author of *A Long Walk to Water* used or altered history in the novel?

Texts used: "One Day I Had to Run" by John Deng Langbany and *A Long Walk to Water* by Linda Sue Park

Similarities	Evidence: *A Long Walk to Water*	Evidence: Informational text
Many of the major events are described similarly in both texts chased from the refugee camp in Ethiopia to cross the Gilo river	On pages 74 and 75, Salva describes how the soldiers fired their guns into the air and chased the people away from the camp toward the Gilo river.	In the informational text, John Deng Langbany also describes how they were chased to the edge of the Gilo river by people shooting at them.
treated poorly at Kakuma by the local people	On page 84, Salva describes how the local people "would often sneak in and steal from the refugees. Sometimes fights broke out, and people were hurt or killed."	John Deng Langbany says that, "In Kakuma, the native people treated us badly because they didn't know us."
challenging big group journey from Sudan to Ethiopia	In chapters 1–11, Salva describes the horrors of the journey from Sudan to Ethiopia in detail.	John Deng Langbany briefly describes how he "ran with thousands of other young children in a very hard journey we made it across the desert all the way to Ethiopia."

Differences	Evidence: *A Long Walk to Water*	Evidence: Informational Text	Possible Reasons for Difference?
How the experience at the Gilo river was described	On page 75 when describing his concerns about crossing the river, he focuses on the current and the crocodiles. He explains, "It was the rainy season. Swollen by the rains, the Gilo's current would be merciless." On page 77 when describing being on the riverbank ready to cross, he tells the story of a man who was taken by a crocodile. "Then Salva saw the telltale flick of a crocodile's tail as it flopped into the water near the young man. Moments later, the man's head jerked oddly—once, twice."	When John Deng Langbany describes being chased from the refugee camp, he describes how he couldn't swim so he watched people being killed and cried as he saw them get shot. He doesn't mention the crocodiles at all.	1. The author of *A Long Walk to Water* wasn't there, and while she listened to Salva's stories to write the book, she wasn't there to know what to emphasize. 2. John Deng Langbany and Salva are two different boys perhaps of different ages who, as a result, may have experienced the event differently based on their own fears.
The balance of time spent on describing the journey from Sudan to Ethiopia	In chapters 1–11, Salva describes the horrors of the journey from Sudan to Ethiopia in detail.	John Deng Langbany briefly describes how he "ran with thousands of other young children in a very hard journey we made it across the desert all the way to Ethiopia."	3. John Deng Langbany was five years old and therefore may not remember much about the journey as much as the places he stayed at, while Salva was eleven and probably remembers a lot more of the journey.

Using History in *A Long Walk to Water*

The Second Sudanese Civil War was a tragedy for millions. Thousands of boys fled the fighting and walked through three countries searching for safety. They were called the "Lost Boys." Their story is unforgettable and has been told many ways. *A Long Walk To Water*, a novel by Linda Sue Park, tells the story of Salva. In the author's note, Park explains, "some of the details in this story have been fictionalized, but the major events depicted are based on Salva's own experiences." John Deng Langbany's article "One Day I Had to Run" is about a similar journey. His article is nonfiction. Comparing the two texts shows how Park used historical events in the novel. Many of the same major events are described in both texts. However, the authors focus their attention differently in the two accounts.

The novel and Langbany's article discuss similar events. For example, both texts describe the journey from Sudan to the United States. Both also describe the walk from Sudan to the first refugee camp in Ethiopia. In chapters 1–11 of *A Long Walk to Water*, Salva describes the horrors of the long journey in detail. He includes hunger, thirst, and people dying. Langbany also describes "a very hard journey" across the desert to Ethiopia. Both texts also discuss how they were treated at Kakuma. In *A Long Walk to Water*, Salva says that the local people "would often sneak in and steal from the refugees" (84). Similarly, Langbany recalls that, "the native people treated us badly because they didn't know us." Park clearly based her novel on real events.

While Park hasn't changed history, she does focus her attention differently from Langbany. For example, most of *A Long Walk to Water* describes the journey from Sudan to Ethiopia. Only chapter 13 is about the journey from Ethiopia to Kenya. However, Langbany focuses nearly half of his article on this part of the journey. Another difference is the description of when the boys are forced to swim the Gilo River. In *A Long Walk to Water*, Salva describes the current and the crocodiles as the most serious threats they faced. In contrast, Langbany focuses on the threat of being shot. The events are the same. But the dangers are described differently. Park focuses on how harsh nature can be. Langbany focuses on the danger from humans.

Although the article and the novel focus on different parts of the journey, they discuss similar events. There are probably many reasons for the differences in focus. One reason may be that Langbany and Salva were different ages during the time described. This means that they had different views. Even if they went through the same events, they would have experienced them differently. Regardless, it is clear that Park found meaning in historical events. In her novel, she uses the experiences of real people like Salva to offer an inspiring message of hope and perseverance.

880L

Painted Essay® Template

W.7.2

Name: _____ **Date:**_____

The Painted Essay®

A tool for teaching basic essay form

Introduction (RED)
Catches readers' attention and gives some background information

FOCUS STATEMENT (GREEN)	
Point 1 (YELLOW)	Point 2 (BLUE)

Proof Paragraph 1 (YELLOW)
Gives evidence and reasons to support Point 1

Proof Paragraph 2
Transition between the ideas in Proof Paragraph 1 and the ideas in Proof Paragraph 2 (BLUE and YELLOW).
Gives evidence and reasons to support Point 2 (BLUE)

Conclusion (GREEN)
What?
So what?

Entrance Ticket: Unit 2, Lesson 8

RL.7.4

Name: _____ **Date:**_____

Directions: As you enter class, respond to the following prompts.

Read the following sentence from the article "The 'Lost Girls' of Sudan."

"Grace and thousands of other Sudanese children—most of them boys— **staggered** out of their war-torn homeland to Kenya in 1992."

What does the word **staggered** tell you about how the children are moving and how they are feeling? What is the connotation of the word **staggered**? (If necessary, consult a dictionary to define the word.)

_____

_____

_____

_____

_____

_____

_____

Synopsis: *A Long Walk to Water*, Chapter 15

RL.7.2

Name: _____ **Date:** _____

- The men kept drilling to get to the clean water.

- They are going to have to dig more, put in pipes, make a foundation with gravel, install the pump, and pour cement around it.

- Salva takes a truck from Ifo to Nairobi to fill out forms, take photos, and get a medical examination.

- Salva's old clothes were threadbare.

- Salva was given new clothes and learned about winter and cold in Rochester, New York.

- Salva took three planes: 1) Nairobi to Frankfurt, Germany 2) Germany to New York City 3) New York City to Rochester.

- He was offered Coca Cola on the plane, which reminded him of his father.

- Salva meets his new, smiling family, and they give him a warm jacket to wear in the cold Rochester winter.

- Salva is emotional as he leaves the airport and reflects on all that he's leaving behind in Sudan.

Similarities and Differences: *A Long Walk to Water* and "The 'Lost Girls' of Sudan" Note-Catcher

RL.7.1, RL.7.9, RI.7.1

Name: _____ **Date:**_____

Use this chart to track how *A Long Walk to Water* and "The 'Lost Girls' of Sudan" treat their subjects similarly and differently.

Event or topic:	
How *A Long Walk to Water* treats it (if at all):	How "The 'Lost Girls' of Sudan" treats it (if at all):
Reflect: How did Linda Sue Park use or alter history in her fictional novel?	

Event or topic:

How *A Long Walk to Water* treats it (if at all):	How "The 'Lost Girls' of Sudan" treats it (if at all):

Reflect: How did Linda Sue Park use or alter history in her fictional novel?

Event or topic:	
How *A Long Walk to Water* treats it (if at all):	How "The 'Lost Girls' of Sudan" treats it (if at all):

Reflect: How did Linda Sue Park use or alter history in her fictional novel?

Event or topic:

How *A Long Walk to Water* treats it (if at all):	How "The 'Lost Girls' of Sudan" treats it (if at all):

Reflect: How did Linda Sue Park use or alter history in her fictional novel?

Event or topic:	
How *A Long Walk to Water* treats it (if at all):	How "The 'Lost Girls' of Sudan" treats it (if at all):

Reflect: How did Linda Sue Park use or alter history in her fictional novel?

Event or topic:

How *A Long Walk to Water* treats it (if at all):	How "The 'Lost Girls' of Sudan" treats it (if at all):

Reflect: How did Linda Sue Park use or alter history in her fictional novel?

So What?

Now look back at the reflections you recorded. What patterns do you notice? Why do you think Linda Sue Park chose to use historical events in this way?

_____

_____

_____

_____

_____

_____

_____

_____

_____

_____

_____

_____

_____

_____

_____

_____

_____

_____

Entrance Ticket: Unit 2, Lesson 9

W.7.2a

Name: _____ **Date:** _____

Directions: As you enter class, respond to the following prompts.

Read this lesson's learning target:

I can plan the introduction of a compare and contrast essay with a strong focus statement.

What is the purpose of the introduction of an essay? What is the purpose of the focus statement?

_____

_____

_____

_____

_____

_____

_____

Language Dive: Compare and Contrast Model Essay, Focus Statement Note-Catcher

RL.7.9, W.7.2a, L.7.1a

Name: _____ **Date:**_____

Comparing the two texts shows how Park used historical events in the novel.

1. Create a complete sentence by filling in the boxes to compare two different things, showing how they are alike.

Comparing		and		shows how they both have happy endings.

Sketch something showing how the two things you compared have happy endings.

2. Complete the sentence frame to compare Salva and Nya's story in your own words:

Comparing Salva and Nya's story shows how _____

_____.

Informative Writing Plan Graphic Organizer

W.7.2

Name: _____ **Date:**_____

Focus Question: _____

_____

Focus

What is the main idea of your piece?

_____

_____

Introduction

How will you catch the reader's attention?

_____

_____

_____

What context do you need to give your reader?

_____

_____

_____

_____

_____

_____

_____

Write your focus statement.

_____

_____

_____

What are the main points you will be making to support this focus?

_____

_____

_____

_____

Proof Paragraph(s) for Point 1

What is the first point that supports your focus statement?

_____

_____

Evidence

What evidence from the texts supports this point?

_____

_____

_____

_____

How does this evidence support this point?

_____

_____

_____

_____

Proof Paragraph(s) for Point 2

What is the next point that supports your focus statement?

_____

_____

Evidence

What evidence from the texts supports this point?

_____

_____

_____

_____

How does this evidence support this point?

_____

_____

_____

_____

Conclusion

Restate your focus statement from the introduction.

_____

_____

What are your further reflections on this topic?

_____

_____

_____

_____

My Sources

List any sources you used in planning your writing.

_____

_____

_____

_____

_____

Informative Writing Checklist

W.7.2, W.7.4, W.7.9, L.7.1, L.7.2, L.7.3, L.7.7

Name: _____ **Date:**_____

Standard	Characteristics of an Effective Informative Writing Piece	Characteristics of This Informative Writing	Date Completed
W.7.9, R.7.1	My focus shows that I clearly understand the topic or text and is well supported with evidence from reliable sources.		
W.7.2a	I provide a clear focus and maintain the focus consistently throughout the piece.		
W.7.2a	I introduce the topic clearly, giving readers a preview of the piece.		
W.7.2f	I have a conclusion that supports the information presented.		

Standard	Characteristics of an Effective Informative Writing Piece	Characteristics of This Informative Writing	Date Completed
W.7.2a	I use strategies such as definition, classification, comparison/contrast, and cause/effect to organize information.		
W.7.2c	I use appropriate transitions to show how ideas and information connect.		
W.7.2b	I use relevant facts, definitions, details, quotations, and examples to explain my thinking.		
W.7.2a	I use formatting, illustrations, and multimedia to help the reader understand information and ideas.		
W.7.2d, L.7.7	I use precise language and domain-specific vocabulary.		

Entrance Ticket: Unit 2, Lesson 10

W.7.2b

Name: _____ **Date:** _____

Directions: As you enter class, respond to the following prompts.

Take another look at the focus statements you drafted yesterday. What would be the opposite or a different version of your focus statement? What kind of evidence would you look for to support this different version of your focus statement?

_____

_____

_____

_____

_____

_____

_____

Entrance Ticket: Unit 2, Lesson 11

W.7.2f

Name: _____ Date:_____

Directions: As you enter class, respond to the following prompts.

Now that you have planned your introductions and Proof Paragraphs, how would you briefly describe your essay to someone else? What is the gist of it?

_____

_____

_____

_____

_____

Language Dive: Compare and Contrast Model Essay, Conclusion Note-Catcher

W.7.2f

Name: _____ Date:_____

Although the article and the novel focus on different parts of the journey, they discuss similar events.

1. Complete the sentence frame below by writing one thing you liked about the novel *A Long Walk to Water* and one thing you didn't like.

Although I really liked		I didn't like	

Sketch one thing you liked about the novel, and one thing you didn't like.

2. Complete the sentence frame to compare and contrast the article and the novel.

Although the article and the novel _____

_____,

they _____

_____.

Entrance Ticket: Unit 2, Lessons 12–13

W.7.2

Name: _____ **Date:** _____

Directions: As you enter class, respond to the following prompts.

Read this learning target:

I can write an essay comparing and contrasting the events in *A Long Walk to Water* with a historical account of the same events.

How have the previous lessons prepared you for this goal?

_____

_____

_____

_____

_____

_____

_____

Track Progress: Informative Writing

Name: _____ **Date:**_____

Learning Target: I can write an informative text.

Standard I'm Tracking: W.7.2

1. How am I doing?

    –   For each criterion, self-assess by putting a check mark in the appropriate column.

    –   Write the number of each standard on a sticky note or flag. Then, in your own writing, place each sticky note in an area that shows evidence you have met that criterion. Make sure you have evidence for each criterion.

    –   Strive to be honest with yourself. Remember, your ability grows with your effort, so it's fine if you aren't there yet!

You will receive feedback on different-colored sticky notes/flags, and in a different-colored pen on the checklist.

Standard	Characteristics of an Effective Informative Piece	4 Advanced	3 Proficient	2 Developing	1 Beginning
W.7.9, R.7.1	My focus shows that I clearly understand the topic or text and is well supported with evidence from reliable sources.				
W.7.2a	I provide a clear focus and maintain the focus consistently throughout the piece.				
W.7.2a	I introduce the topic clearly, giving readers a preview of the piece.				
W.7.2f	I have a conclusion that supports the information presented.				

Standard	Characteristics of an Effective Informative Piece	4 Advanced	3 Proficient	2 Developing	1 Beginning
W.7.2a	I use strategies such as definition, classification, comparison/contrast, and cause/effect to organize information.				
W.7.2c	I use appropriate transitions to show how ideas and information connect.				
W.7.2b	I use relevant facts, definitions, details, quotations, and examples to explain my thinking.				
W.7.2a	I use formatting, illustrations, and multimedia to help the reader understand information and ideas.				
W.7.2d, L.7.7	I use precise language and domain-specific vocabulary.				
W.7.4 (partial), W.7.2e	I use a formal style.				
L.7.3	I use language that expresses my ideas concisely.				
L.7.1	My words and sentences follow the rules of writing.				
L.7.2	The spelling, capitalization, and punctuation are correct.				

2. How have I improved since I last worked on this skill?

_____

_____

_____

Teacher Response:

_____

_____

_____

3. How can I improve next time?

_____

_____

_____

Teacher Response:

_____

_____

_____

Anchor Standard

W.2

By the end of Grade 12 I will be able to: write informative/explanatory texts to examine and convey complex ideas and information clearly and accurately through the effective selection, organization, and analysis of content.

Entrance Ticket: Unit 2, Lesson 14

W.7.2c

Name: _____ **Date:**_____

Directions: As you enter class, respond to the following prompts.

Read the following sentences from the model essay with some words removed:

Many of the same major events are described in both texts. _____ the authors focus their attention differently in the two accounts.

_____ Salva describes the current and the crocodiles as the most serious threats they faced. _____ John Deng Langbany focuses on the threat of being shot.

What kinds of words are missing from these sentences? How does removing these words impact the sentences?

_____

_____

_____

_____

_____

_____

_____

Language Dive: Compare and Contrast Model Essay, Transitions Note-Catcher

W.7.2c

Name: _____ **Date:**_____

Similarly, Langbany recalls that, "the native people treated us badly because they didn't know us."

1. Complete the sentence frame below by writing something that is also very blue.

The sky is very blue. Similarly,		is very blue.

Sketch something that is also very blue, similar to the sky.

2. Complete the sentence frame by replacing **similarly** with another adverb that means the same thing, and then complete the sentence in your own words.

_____, Langbany recalls that _____

_____.

Directions for Peer Critique

W.7.5

Name: _____ **Date:** _____

1. Exchange essays with your partner.

2. Circle transition words and places where transition words should be included. Also identify examples where spelling needs to be corrected.

3. Generate suggestions for transition words and spelling changes in the margins of your partner's essay.

4. Identify one star (one thing your partner did well) and record it on a sticky note.

   – Example: "I noticed you spelled these difficult words correctly and included a transition word in your focus statement."

5. Identify one step (one thing your partner could improve) and record it on a different-colored sticky note.

   – Example: "Could you include a transition word in the first sentence of the second paragraph to make the flow of your ideas clearer?"

6. Give back your partner's essay.

7. Take turns explaining your feedback.

8. Ask your partner clarifying questions if you don't understand.

Unit 3

Entrance Ticket: Unit 3, Lesson 1

L.7.4

Name: _____ **Date:_____**

Directions: As you enter class, answer the following prompts.

Read this learning target, and underline the words **techniques**, **version**, **audio**, and **effect**:

I can compare and contrast a written story to the audio version of the story and analyze the effect of the techniques.

Use the vocabulary strategies on the Close Readers Do These Things anchor chart to find the meanings of these words: **techniques**, **version**, **audio**, and **effect**. Record the meanings in your vocabulary log.

What are some ways that listening to something read is different from reading it? What can a reader do that words on a page can't do alone?

_____

_____

_____

_____

_____

_____

Synopsis: *A Long Walk to Water*, Chapter 16

RL.7.2

Name: _____ **Date:** _____

- The men and Nya's father clear the land in front of Nya's house for a new building.

- Salva notices how different life is in America with the paved roads, electricity, and all of the white people.

- He finds studying to be calming, and his new family is kind.

- Salva's English improves slowly with hard work and time.

- Salva has spent six years in Rochester, where he studies business and plays volleyball.

- He has an idea that he would like to return to Sudan to help people.

- Salva receives an email from a cousin that his father is alive and in a clinic because of a stomach surgery.

- His father is in a remote part of southern Sudan.

- It takes months of planning for Salva to be able to return to Sudan.

- Salva flies to New York City, Amsterdam, and then Kampala, Uganda, and then onto Juba, Sudan.

- Everything feels the same, and yet everything feels different.

- Finally, Salva arrives at a makeshift hospital and asks for his father.

Compare Audio to Text: *A Long Walk to Water,* Chapter 16 Note-Catcher

RL.7.1, RL.7.7

Name: _____ **Date:** _____

Directions: Use this note-catcher and answer the questions below to analyze the effects of the techniques used in an audio version of a text.

Text: pages 100–101; audio: 2:11:36–2:12:28

First Listen (record your first thoughts and questions here):

_____

_____

_____

1. **Part A**

   What do you notice about the way the reader reads the phrases beginning ". . . United Nations clinic . . . your father . . ." on page 100? Choose two.

   A. The voice remains the same.

   B. The voice has a different accent.

   C. The sound of the voice changes.

   D. The voice is from a different character.

   E. The tone of the voice becomes angry.

   Part B

   What do you notice about the text for these words?

   _____

   _____

   _____

Part C

What idea are both the author and the reader trying to convey with how they write and speak the words in this excerpt?

A.   Salva's thoughts as he reads the email

B.   Salva's hearing the other characters in the house

C.   Salva's memories of when he met his cousin

D.   Salva's conversation on the phone

2.   Reread these sentences from page 100: "My father!" he shouted. "They have found my father!"

   What are the ways the writer shows Salva's emotions with these sentences?

   _____

   _____

   _____

   How does the reader show emotion?

   _____

   _____

   _____

3.   Reflection: Based on these questions, how are the written text and the audio version related? What should a good reader do when they see the text written in certain ways?

   _____

   _____

   _____

   _____

   _____

Complete the chart to compare and contrast the audio and text versions of chapter 16 of *A Long Walk to Water*.

Effect	Technique: Book	Technique: Audio	Example

Entrance Ticket: Unit 3, Lesson 2

RL.7.7

Name: _____ **Date:** _____

Directions: As you enter class, answer the following prompts.

1. Read this learning target, and rewrite the learning target using your own words in place of the words **version**, **audio**, **techniques**, and **effect**:

    I can compare and contrast a written story to the audio version of the story and analyze the effect of the techniques.

    _____

    _____

    _____

2. Write a learning target for yourself for today using a character trait.

    _____

    _____

    _____

3. Return to chapter 9 of *A Long Walk to Water*, and select a paragraph or sentence that you would like to read aloud for the class. Mark it with a sticky note. Think about how you will read the paragraph or sentence to emphasize emotion and action in the text. Only volunteers will read. If you would rather not read in front of the class, select a paragraph or sentence and think about how it would be read aloud. What can a reader add to the written text?

    _____

    _____

    _____

Synopsis: *A Long Walk to Water*, Chapter 17

RL.7.2

Name: _____ **Date:**_____

- Nya's father tells her that they're building a school for boys *and* girls.

- With the well, girls no longer have to walk to the pond, so they can now be educated.

- Salva introduces himself to his dad in the hospital, but his dad doesn't recognize him right away.

- It has been 19 years since they've seen one another.

- Salva's father, Mawien Dut, sprinkles water on Salva's head as a Dinka blessing for someone who is lost and then found again.

- Everyone was sure that Salva was dead, but Mawien Dut never gave up hope that he was alive.

- Salva's mother is back in the village.

- Salva's sisters are all fine, too, but of his three brothers, only one survived.

- Salva's father's illness is from years of drinking contaminated water.

- As Salva and his father hug goodbye, they cry.

- Salva has an idea to help Southern Sudan. He asks many people for help and speaks to many audiences about his idea, but we don't know what his idea is yet.

Compare Audio to Text: *A Long Walk to Water*, Chapter 17 Note-Catcher

RL.7.1, RL.7.7

Name: _____ **Date:** _____

Directions: Use this note-catcher and answer the questions to analyze the effects of the techniques used in an audio version of a text.

Text: pages 103–104; audio: 2:15:30–2:17:04

First Listen (Record your first thoughts and questions here.)

_____

_____

_____

1. **Part A**

   What do you notice about how the reader reads the dialogue for Nya and her father?

   _____

   _____

   _____

   Part B

   How does this way of speaking help the listener?

   A. by making it easier to tell who is speaking

   B. by explaining the characters' actions

   C. by showing how the characters are related

   D. by creating suspense with tone of voice

2. How would you describe the way the reader says Nya's questions on page 103: "*All* the children, Papa? The girls, too?"

   _____

   _____

   _____

3. **Part A**

   How does the reader's tone of voice change as the chapter goes on?

   A. It becomes more excited.

   B. It becomes more serious.

   C. It becomes more confused.

   D. It becomes more disappointed.

   Part B

   What are some of the ways the author shows the reader what tone to read in? (Hint: Refer back to questions on the Compare Audio to Text: *A Long Walk to Water*, Chapter 16 note-catcher.)

   _____

   _____

   _____

4. Reflection: Based on what you've read so far, how do the text and audio versions show when the book is switching narrators? How can you use these techniques to help you when you write and read your narratives aloud?

   _____

   _____

   _____

   _____

   _____

   _____

   _____

   _____

   _____

   _____

   _____

Complete the chart to compare and contrast the audio and text versions of chapter 17 of *A Long Walk to Water*.

Effect	Technique: Book	Technique: Audio	Example

Language Dive: *A Long Walk to Water*, Page 103 Note-Catcher

RL.7.7

Name: _____ **Date:** _____

When at last she was able to speak, it was only in a whisper.

1. Complete the sentence frame below by writing about how you felt when you were finally able to do something.

When at last I		I couldn't stop smiling.

Sketch something you were finally able to do that made you smile.

2. Complete the sentence frame below to describe how you think Nya felt when she finally went to school.

    When at last Nya went to school, she _____

    _____.

Entrance Ticket: Unit 3, Lesson 3

RL.7.7

Name: _____ **Date:**_____

Directions: As you enter class, answer the following prompt.

Now that you have practiced comparing and contrasting audio and texts, what are some of the ways authors show readers how to read texts?

_____

_____

_____

_____

_____

_____

_____

_____

Entrance Ticket: Unit 3, Lesson 4

RL.7.4, L.7.5c

Name: _____ **Date:_____**

Directions: As you enter class, answer the following prompts.

"Little Kuol . . . Salva closed his eyes for a few moments, trying to picture his brothers through a **haze** of time and grief." (106)

What does the word **haze** tell you about what Salva was experiencing? What is the connotation of the word **haze**?

_____

_____

_____

_____

_____

_____

_____

Synopsis: *A Long Walk to Water*, Chapter 18

RL.7.2

Name: _____ **Date:** _____

- Nya's village finds out that students from an American school raised the money to dig the well.

- Everyone drinks the clear, cool water and celebrates.

- In a few days, the school will be completed, and in a year, they will build a marketplace and someday a clinic.

- The well brings all of this good fortune to the village.

- The well will be used by Sudanese for miles around, and no one will ever be refused water.

- Nya thanks the Dinka boss for bringing water to her Nuer village.

- The boss turns out to be Salva, who has drilled many wells for the Dinka, and this year decided to drill one for the Nuer.

Narrative Writing Plan Graphic Organizer

W.7.3

Name: _____ **Date:** _____

Use this organizer to keep track of the material needed for your narrative.

Part I: Think about Purpose

Task (what I'm writing)

_____

_____

_____

Purpose (why I am writing it)

_____

_____

_____

Audience (who I am writing it for)

_____

_____

_____

Part II: Build a Character and Setting(s)

Description	**Habits of Character**
(How old is your main character? Character traits—serious, humorous, rebellious, follower, leader, etc. Does he or she have any special talents or interests, such as music or art?)	(Character traits—What are the habits of character that help your character along the way? How does your character deal with problems?)
Life Before the War and the Journey	**Descriptions of the Setting(s)**
(What is your character's background? What were his or her days like before the war started? What was his or her home like?)	(What are some of the areas from the journey you'd like to write about?)
Sources	

Part III: Plan a Plot

Background

_____

_____

_____

Event or Action

_____

_____

_____

Event or Action

_____

_____

_____

Event or Action

_____

_____

_____

Climax

_____

_____

_____

Reflection

_____

_____

_____

Ending

_____

_____

_____

Sources

_____

_____

_____

_____

_____

_____

Part IV: Pacing

What to focus on? Event from the plot where I should slow things down:	Description (pausing to describe something to slow down time for the reader)	Dialogue (using speech to slow down a moment and focus the reader)

Words I can use to pass time quickly (transition words):

Narrative Writing Checklist

Name: _____ Date: _____

Learning Target: I can write a narrative text.

Standard I'm Tracking: W.7.3

Standard	Characteristics of an Effective Narrative	Characteristics of This Narrative	Date Completed
W.7.9	I effectively use information from sources to craft the characters, setting, and events in the narrative.	My story shows that I used the information from *A Long Walk to Water* and other texts to create my narrative.	
W.7.3a	I engage and orient the reader by effectively establishing context.	I start the story with an interesting scene and make it clear to the reader where and when the story is happening.	
W.7.3a	I introduce a narrator and/or characters, and establish a point of view.	Throughout my story, I show the point of view of my characters as they make their journey.	
W.7.3e	I provide a conclusion that follows from and reflects on the events or experiences in the narrative.	My ending is related to what happens in the rest of the story and helps to explain what the story is about.	
W.7.3a	I organize events in a sequence that unfolds naturally and logically.	My story is easy to follow because I have shown how one event leads to another.	
W.7.3c, W.7.4	I use a variety of transitional words and phrases to sequence events, and to show changes in time or in setting.	When I jump ahead in time, I use words and phrases to show this. I also let the reader know when my characters enter a new setting.	

Standard	Characteristics of an Effective Narrative	Characteristics of This Narrative	Date Completed
W.7.3b	I develop experiences, events, and characters using dialogue and description.	During the moments I want to focus on, I use dialogue and description to show more about the events and characters in my story.	
W.7.3b	I "slow down" important events by adding detail and "speed up" events that are not important.	I use dialogue and description to slow down some events and transitional words and phrases to speed up other events.	
W.7.3d, W.7.4	I use descriptive details, sensory language, precise wording to capture the action and convey experiences and events.	I carefully choose the descriptive words I use to show what my characters are going through on their journey.	
L.7.1	My words and sentences follow the rules of writing.	I make sure as I write and revise that my writing is clear and follows the rules.	
L.7.2	The spelling, capitalization, and punctuation are correct.	I make sure as I write and revise that everything is spelled, capitalized, and punctuated correctly.	

Entrance Ticket: Unit 3, Lesson 5

W.7.3a

Name: _____ **Date:** _____

Directions: As you enter class, answer the following prompts.

Read this learning target:

I can create accurate settings based on the places I have read about.

Why is it important to create accurate settings for this narrative? Do all narratives need to have settings based on real life?

_____

_____

_____

_____

_____

_____

Synopsis: *A Long Walk to Water,* Ending Sections

RL.7.2

Name: _____ **Date:** _____

Message from Salva

• The book is his true story.

• He would like for everyone to know more about the Lost Boys and Sudan.

• He is grateful to the United Nations, International Red Cross, Moore family, Episcopal Church, Rochester, Monroe Community College, Water for Sudan, Inc., Board of Water for Sudan, and Rotary Clubs.

• He knows that hope and perseverance helped him overcome obstacles.

Author's Note

• Some events in the story have been fictionalized, but the majority is Salva's true story.

• Nya's part was created through interviews with villagers, as well as studying video footage and looking at photographs.

• The Second Sudanese Civil War occurred in 1983 and was the conflict between the Muslims in the north and the non-Muslims in the south.

• Millions were killed, imprisoned, tortured, and enslaved.

• Millions were unable to return to their homes.

• Hundreds of thousands of Lost Boys, like Salva, walked in search of safety.

• Upon returning home after the conflict, many found their families gone.

• Others lived for years in refugee camps, like Salva.

• Some were finally reunited with their families after decades of separation.

• In 2002, the United States passed the Sudan Peace Act, which named the Sudanese government responsible for the deaths of more than 2 million people.

• Three years later peace occurred between the North and the South.

• The South was able to govern itself.

• There is a war in Darfur between the Arabs and the Africans in the western part of Sudan, which is separate from the north/south conflict.

- Salva reunited with his family twice more, including with his cousins, the children of his uncle.

- He has also reunited with other Lost Boys in Rochester.

- As of 2014, Salva's organization, Water for South Sudan, drilled 250 wells.

- Salva now lives in South Sudan.

- The author traveled to South Sudan to see Salva's work and is grateful to call Salva a friend.

Addendum, 2015

- People have been inspired by Salva's story.

- Schools have developed fundraisers for Sudan.

- Salva and Linda would like to thank everyone for their efforts, as they are saving people's lives.

- If you would like to help, visit https://www.waterforsouthsudan.org/.

Entrance Ticket: Unit 3, Lesson 6

W.7.3a

Name: _____ **Date:**_____

Directions: As you enter class, answer the following prompt.

Now that you have been thinking about the plot of your story, what do you think is the best way to start the story and show readers the setting and characters?

_____

_____

_____

_____

_____

_____

Language Dive: *Nasreen's Secret School,* Page 22 Note-Catcher

RL.7.4, L.7.5, W.7.3e

Name: _____ **Date:** _____

Now she can see **blue sky beyond those dark clouds**.

Sketch the figurative meaning of the chunk: **blue sky beyond those dark clouds.** Next to it, sketch the literal meaning of this chunk.

1. Complete the sentence frame to write about something you feel hopeful about, using figurative language.

Now I can see		beyond	

2. Complete the sentence frame to make up your own concluding sentence about Salva's story in *A Long Walk to Water.*

Salva saw_____ beyond _____

_____.

Nasreen's Secret School Plot Map

W.7.3

Name: _____ **Date:** _____

Part III: Plan a Plot

Background

Herat was a beautiful city but the soldiers ruined it for people, especially girls who couldn't go to school.

Event or Action

Soldiers take Nasreen's father away, and her mother disappears, too.

Event or Action

Nasreen stops speaking.

Event or Action

Nasreen's grandmother puts her in school. She doesn't speak to anyone for a long time.

Climax

Nasreen speaks to her friend Mina!

Reflection

Nasreen begins learning more and showing her grandmother.

Ending

Though they still miss Nasreen's parents, Nasreen's grandmother is happy Nasreen has an education.

Sources

_____

_____

_____

_____

_____

Entrance Ticket: Unit 3, Lesson 7

W.7.3b

Name: _____ **Date:** _____

Directions: As you enter class, answer the following question.

Based on the plot chart you filled out in the previous lesson, what is one event from your story that you would want the reader to pay close attention to?

_____

_____

_____

_____

_____

_____

Narrative Transition Words and Phrases

W.7.3c

Name: _____ **Date:**_____

Time	Space
then	here
next	there
later	over there
even so	under
soon	above
meanwhile	behind
eventually	beyond
suddenly	in the distance
later on	not far away
after that	
finally	

Entrance Ticket: Unit 3, Lesson 8

W.7.4

Name: _____ **Date:**_____

Directions: As you enter class, answer the following questions.

Now that you have been planning your narratives and are ready to draft them for a third-grade elementary school audience, what are some of the ways you can make the stories appealing to younger audiences? How will you add these elements into your story?

_____

_____

_____

_____

_____

_____

Track Progress: Narrative Writing

Name: _____ **Date:** _____

Learning Target: I can write a narrative text.

Standards I'm Tracking: W.7.3

1. How am I doing?

    – For each criterion, self-assess by putting a check mark in the
    appropriate column.

    – Write the number of each standard on a sticky note or flag. Then, in
    your own writing, place each sticky note in an area that shows evidence
    you have met that criterion. Make sure you have evidence for each
    criterion.

    – Strive to be honest with yourself. Remember, your ability grows with
    your effort, so it's fine if you aren't there yet!

You will receive feedback on different-colored sticky notes/flags, and in a
different-colored pen on the checklist.

Standard	Characteristics of an Effective Narrative	4 Advanced	3 Proficient	2 Developing	1 Beginning
W.7.9	I effectively use information from sources to craft the characters, setting, or events in the narrative.				
W.7.3a	I engage and orient the reader by effectively establishing context.				
W.7.3a	I introduce a narrator and/or characters and establish a point of view.				
W.7.3e	I provide a conclusion that follows from and reflects on the events or experiences in the narrative.				

Standard	Characteristics of an Effective Narrative	4 Advanced	3 Proficient	2 Developing	1 Beginning
W.7.3a	I organize events in a sequence that unfolds naturally and logically.				
W.7.3c, W.7.4	I use a variety of transitional words and phrases to sequence events and to show changes in time or in setting.				
W.7.3b	I develop experiences, events and characters using dialogue and description.				
W.7.3b	I "slow down" important events by adding detail and "speed up" events that are not important.				
W.7.3d, W.7.4	I use descriptive details, sensory language, and precise wording to capture the action and convey experiences and events.				
L.7.1	My words and sentences follow the rules of writing.				
L.7.2	The spelling, capitalization, and punctuation are correct.				

2. How have I improved since I last worked on this skill?

_____

_____

_____

Teacher Response:

_____

_____

_____

3. How can I improve next time?

_____

_____

_____

Teacher Response:

_____

_____

_____

Anchor Standards

W.3

By the end of Grade 12 I will be able to: write narratives to develop real or imagined experiences or events using effective technique, well-chosen details, and well-structured event sequences.

Entrance Ticket: Unit 3, Lesson 9

RI.7.6

Name: _____ **Date:**_____

Directions: Reread the final sentence from the author's note of *A Long Walk to Water*: "Keep reading . . . and walk the walk!" (121) Answer the following questions:

What did these words mean to you when you read them? How do they help to explain the purpose of the book?

_____

_____

_____

_____

_____

_____

_____

Entrance Ticket: Unit 3, Lessons 10–11

Name: _____ **Date:**_____

Directions: Answer the following questions.

Now that you are ready to convert your narratives into ebooks, think about some of the different ways you've read text (books, phones, computers, magazines). How do those ways of reading affect your experience? What do you think will be most interesting or useful about an ebook?

_____

_____

_____

_____

_____

_____

_____

Grade 7: Module 1

Homework Resources (for Families)

Unit 1: Build Background Knowledge: The Lost Boys of the Sudan

Common Core State Standards addressed:

- RL.7.2, RL.7.3, RL.7.4, RL.7.6, RL.7.10
- SL.7.1, SL.7.1a, SL.7.1b, SL.7.1c
- L.7.4, L.7.4a, L.7.4b, L.7.4c, L.7.4d, L.7.6

 ## Guiding Questions and Big Ideas

Who are The Lost Boys of the Sudan, and what is their story?

- *The second Sudanese civil war displaced millions of people, including hundreds of thousands of Lost Boys who walked through southern Sudan, Ethiopia, and Kenya in search of a safe haven.*

What are the habits of character the Lost Boys used to survive?

- *The Lost Children persevered to overcome the hardships of war, starvation, thirst, displacement, and threats by wild animals. Many of them show respect, empathy, and integrity as they help each other survive these same hardships. Some of them have also become leaders in the United States or in their home country (like Salva and his organization Water for South Sudan), using their strengths to help others grow, helping care for their environment and shared spaces, and using their learning to do so.*

What will your student be doing at school?

Students begin Unit 1 reading the novel *A Long Walk to Water*.[1] The focus of the first half of the unit of reading is catching questions about the conflict described, how the setting shapes the characters and plot, and how an author develops and contrasts the points of view of different characters in the text. In the second half of the unit, students begin to analyze how themes have developed throughout the story so far. Students also create discussion norms in order to have productive discussions about the text at the end of the unit.

Central to the EL Education curriculum is a focus on "habits of character" and social-emotional learning. Students work to become effective learners, developing mindsets and skills for success in college, career, and life (e.g., initiative, responsibility, perseverance, and collaboration); work to become ethical people, treating others well and standing up for what is right (e.g., empathy, integrity, respect, and compassion); and work to contribute to a better world, putting their learning to use to improve communities (e.g., citizenship and service).

In this unit, students focus on respect, empathy, and compassion as they respond to one another's ideas and skills in written work and in discussions. During discussions, students also focus on collaboration and taking initiative. Also, they focus on integrity and perseverance as they work independently on assessments. As they track progress on their assessments, they take responsibility for their own learning.

---

[1] *A Long Walk to Water* contains references to sensitive topics such as war (including the violent death of family members and children), displacement, family separation, hunger, thirst (including death from lack of water), refugee camps, violent deaths from wild animals, and serious illness of family members. The issues presented will be carefully and sensitively discussed to give students context as they read the story. You might speak with your student about this at home both before and after reading the book. Raise any concerns with the teacher.

How can you support your student at home?

Talk with your student about the Lost Boys and Girls of Sudan or other children/people displaced from their homes by war or disasters.

Read chapter books with your student, and discuss how the setting (time and place) develops the characters (people) and plot (events). Also, discuss the different points of view or opinions of the characters in the book and how the author develops those different points of view. Finally, discuss the theme or message the author is communicating through the book. You may use questions such as the following for your conversations:

- What is the setting of this story? How does the setting affect the characters? What must they do and be like to live in this setting?

- From whose point of view or perspective is this story told? How do we know? What is the character/narrator's point of view of ___ (a topic/idea/character in the story)? How do we know?

- What is the theme of this story? What message is the author communicating? What lesson do the characters learn?

Unit 1: Homework

At the beginning of the unit for homework, students read the module guiding questions (listed above) and discuss them with a family member, talking about how the questions make them feel and why, and what the questions make them think about. Students can sketch or write their reflections. Also, students read chapter 1 of *A Long Walk to Water* to prepare for in-class reading and discussion of the chapter.

For homework in this unit, students answer selected response (multiple choice) questions about the plot (or events) happening in chapter 1 of *A Long Walk to Water*. Also, students read chapters of *A Long Walk to Water* to prepare for in-class reading and discussion of the chapters.

For homework in this unit, students use context (the words around a word) and, if necessary, a dictionary to determine the meaning of unfamiliar vocabulary in chapters of *A Long Walk to Water*. Then students record the words and their definitions in the correct section of their vocabulary log. Also, students read chapters *of A Long Walk to Water* to prepare for in-class reading and discussion of the chapters.

In Lessons 9 and 15–16, homework focuses on research reading for which students read a topic-related book of choice and answer a question related to the unit's ideas and skills.

Research Reading: When not reading their anchor text, your student is expected to independently research the topic by reading topic-related books of his or her choice for approximately 20 minutes each day and responding to a prompt of choice in the front of the independent reading journal. These are usually books your student will bring home from school; however, they may be topic-related books chosen by the student at the public or your home library. Prompts for independent reading can be found in the homework materials provided below.

Lesson	Lesson Content	Homework Practice	Due In	Anticipated Date[2]
1	Students participate in the Infer the Topic protocol by engaging with the texts they will read throughout the module. Also, students first encounter the performance task and guiding questions for the module, as well as the module's anchor text.	1. Students complete Homework: Module Guiding Questions anchor chart to read and reflect on the guiding questions for the module. With their family, they talk about how the questions make them feel and why, and what the questions make them think about. Students can sketch or write their reflections. 2. Students read chapter 1 of *A Long Walk to Water* to prepare for in-class reading and discussion of the chapter.	Lesson 2	
2	Students explore the learning targets and discuss the difference between academic and domain-specific words and review dictionary use. Students reflect on the module guiding questions and begin reading the anchor text of the module, *A Long Walk to Water*.	1. Students complete Homework: Selected Response Questions: *A Long Walk to Water*, answering selected response questions about plot unfolding in chapter 1 of *A Long Walk to Water* and identify the strategies used to answer the questions. 2. Students read chapter 2 of *A Long Walk to Water* to prepare for in-class reading and discussion of the chapter.	Lesson 3	
3	Students generate strategies to answer selected response questions. Then they read chapter 2 of *A Long Walk to Water* and analyze how the setting affects the character and plot development. Students conclude the lesson with a discussion about the different points of view of the two main characters: Nya and Salva.	1. Students use context and if necessary, a dictionary to determine the meaning of unfamiliar vocabulary in chapter 2 of *A Long Walk to Water*. Then they record the words and their definitions in the correct section of their vocabulary log. 2. Students read chapter 3 of *A Long Walk to Water* to prepare for in-class reading and discussion of the chapter.	Lesson 4	

[2] Teacher note: Please complete the Anticipated Date column according to your schedule.

Lesson	Lesson Content	Homework Practice	Due In	Anticipated Date[2]
4	Students read chapter 3 of *A Long Walk to Water* and analyze how the setting affects the character and plot development and how the author develops and contrasts different points of view.	1. Students use context, word parts, and if necessary, a dictionary to determine the meaning of unfamiliar vocabulary in chapter 3 of *A Long Walk to Water*. Then they record the words and their definitions in the correct section of their vocabulary log. 2. Students complete Homework: Text-Dependent Questions: *A Long Walk to Water*, Chapter 3, using evidence to support their responses.	Lesson 5	
5	Students participate in a close reading of the article "The Lost Boys of the Sudan," focusing on information related to the Sudanese Civil War and the stories of the Lost Boys, who escaped the fighting and found refuge elsewhere.	1. Students use context and if necessary, a dictionary to determine the meaning of unfamiliar vocabulary in "The Lost Boys of the Sudan." Then they record the words and their definitions in the correct section of their vocabulary log. 2. Students read chapter 4 of *A Long Walk to Water* to prepare for in-class reading and discussion of the chapter.	Lesson 6	
6	Students read chapter 4 of *A Long Walk to Water* and analyze point of view, setting, characters, and plot. Students also choose independent research reading texts according to the teacher's or a suggested plan.	1. Students complete Homework: Analyze Point of View: *A Long Walk to Water*, Chapter 4. 2. Students read chapter 5 of *A Long Walk to Water* to prepare for in-class reading and discussion of the chapter.	Lesson 7	

Lesson	Lesson Content	Homework Practice	Due In	Anticipated Date[2]
7	Students read chapter 5 of *A Long Walk to Water* and analyze how setting shapes character and plot and how the author develops and contrasts Nya's and Salva's points of view.	1. Students use context, word parts, and if necessary, a dictionary to determine the meaning of unfamiliar vocabulary in chapter 5 of *A Long Walk to Water*. Then they record the words and their definitions in the correct section of their vocabulary log. 2. Students read chapter 6 of *A Long Walk to Water* to prepare for in-class reading and discussion of the chapter.	Lesson 8	
8	Students read chapter 6 of *A Long Walk to Water* and analyze how setting shapes plot and characters, and analyze how the author develops and contrasts points of view, including evidence for the mid-unit assessment.	1. Students read chapter 7 of *A Long Walk to Water* to prepare for in-class reading and discussion of the chapter.	Lesson 9	
9	Students read chapter 7 of *A Long Walk to Water* and discuss themes in relation to the novel. Students conclude the lesson by analyzing a model summary and identifying the components of effective summaries.	1. Students read for at least 20 minutes in their independent research reading text. Then they select a prompt and write a response in their independent reading journal.	Lesson 10	
10	Students analyze the author's use of language in greater detail through a Language Dive. Then students delve deeper into analyzing theme and summary in chapter 7 of *A Long Walk to Water*, answering text-dependent questions to help guide their discussion of the theme and strategies for writing a summary.	1. Students complete Homework: Themes and Summary: *A Long Walk to Water*, Chapter 7. 2. Students read chapter 8 of *A Long Walk to Water* to prepare for in-class reading and discussion of the chapter.	Lesson 11	

Lesson	Lesson Content	Homework Practice	Due In	Anticipated Date[2]
11	Students continue their work analyzing theme and writing summaries of *A Long Walk to Water*, focusing on chapter 8.	1. Students complete Homework: Summary and Theme: *A Long Walk to Water*, Chapter 8, answering questions related to the use of language to develop the tone and theme of chapter 8. 2. Students read chapter 9 of *A Long Walk to Water* to prepare for in-class reading and discussion of the chapter.	Lesson 12	
12	In the first part of this end of unit assessment, students demonstrate their understanding of how authors develop theme as well as write an objective summary of chapter 9 of *A Long Walk to Water*.	1. Students read chapter 10 of *A Long Walk to Water* to prepare for in-class reading and discussion of the chapter.	Lesson 13	
13	Students continue their work examining how theme is developed in *A Long Walk to Water*. Then students work together to generate discussion norms based on reflections of their own previous text-based discussions and observations of a group discussion.	1. Students complete Homework: Text-Dependent Questions: *A Long Walk to Water*, Chapter 10, answering questions related to the use of language to develop the tone and theme of chapter 8. 2. Students read chapter 11 of *A Long Walk to Water* to prepare for in-class reading and discussion of the chapter.	Lesson 14	
14	Students read chapter 11 of *A Long Walk to Water* and prepare for the end of unit text-based discussion, in which they will analyze how themes develop in *A Long Walk to Water*.	1. Students read chapter 12 of *A Long Walk to Water* to prepare for in-class reading and discussion of the chapter.	Lessons 15–16	
15–16	Students read chapter 12 of *A Long Walk to Water* and update their Text-Based Discussion note-catchers. Finally, students complete the end of unit assessment, in which they participate in a group discussion about themes in *A Long Walk to Water*.	1. Students read for at least 20 minutes in their independent research reading text. Then they select a prompt and write a response in their independent reading journal.	Unit 2, Lesson 1	

Independent Reading

Directions: Remember to record responses to research reading in the front of your independent reading journal and responses to choice reading in the back. Try to choose a different prompt each time. Record any new vocabulary in your vocabulary log. Underline vocabulary found during independent reading.

Record:

- Date
- Title and author of your reading book
- Pages you have read
- Prompt
- Response

Example:

<u>Date:</u> 09/25/20

<u>Book Title and Author:</u> *A Long Walk to Water* by Linda Sue Park

<u>Pages Read:</u> 51–75

<u>Prompt:</u> How does the setting affect (character/person)? What kind of person does he/she have to be in that setting?

<u>Response:</u> The setting of the desert affects Salva by challenging him almost beyond his limits. He feels he cannot go on, but his uncle tells him to just walk "one painful step at a time" (54). Salva survives the desert with this help from his uncle. This setting makes Salva severely challenged and forces him to be strong, persevere, and rely on the support of others.

Consider using the following independent reading prompts.[3]

- How does this text add to your understanding of one of the guiding questions of the module?

- How does the setting affect (character/person)? What kind of person does he/she have to be in that setting?

- What kind of events does (character/person) experience in the setting?

- From whose point of view is this part of the text told? How does the author develop this person's/character's point of view?

- How does reading from the author's/character's point of view help you understand something about Sudan?

- What theme or central idea is present in the text you read? Give text details that convey that theme or central idea.

- How does (character/person)'s experiences relate to Salva's?

- How does (character/person)'s experiences relate to Nya's?

- How does (character/person) grow and change?

- If you were (character/person), what would you do differently?

- Record two or three facts in your own words that you learned from the text.

- Summarize your research reading today in no more than five sentences.

- What questions do you have about the topic after reading?

- Choose one new word from your reading today and analyze it on a vocabulary square.

[3] Some of the prompts will not be appropriate for the text students are reading. Invite students to choose a prompt that works for the text they have just read.

Definition in your own words	Synonyms (words with the same meaning)
Words with the same affix or root	**Sketch**

Translation in home language (if appropriate)

Vocabulary

Directions: In the classroom, you have been recording words from your texts in your vocabulary log. Throughout this unit, you have been research reading topic-related books at home to build your knowledge of Sudan and recording words in your independent reading journal.

Choose a word from your research reading or from a text you've read in class and add the word to your vocabulary log. Try to choose a different word to add and to practice a different vocabulary strategy each time. For each word, be sure to add the following:

1. The definition, or meaning, of the word

2. The vocabulary strategy you used to figure out the meaning of the word

3. A sketch or diagram that helps you to better understand the meaning of the word

Record new vocabulary in vocabulary logs and mark academic vocabulary with a symbol, for example a star:

- Academic vocabulary: words you might find in informational texts on many different topics. For example, the words evidence and rationale are words that could be found in books on any topic.

- Domain-specific vocabulary: words about a particular topic. For example, the words tadpoles, frogspawn, and amphibian are some that would be found on the topic of frogs.

Vocabulary Strategies

As a reminder, the vocabulary strategies we've been working on in class are:

- Context: Read the sentence around the word.

- Look at the affixes for clues.

- Look at the root of the word for clues.

- Use a dictionary.

- Discuss the word with another person (after attempting some of the above strategies).

Homework: Module Guiding Questions Anchor Chart

Name: _____ **Date:**_____

What thoughts do you have about the guiding questions for the module? Record your thoughts in the Notes column.

Questions and Big Ideas	Notes
• Who are the Lost Boys of Sudan, and what is their story? • What are the habits of character the Lost Boys used to survive? • The second Sudanese civil war displaced millions of people, including hundreds of thousands of Lost Boys who walked through southern Sudan, Ethiopia, and Kenya in search of a safe haven. • Some of the Lost Boys were sent to the United States to begin new lives in safety.	

Homework: Selected Response Questions:
A Long Walk to Water, Chapter 1

Name: _____ **Date:**_____

Underline your answers for the selected response questions. Then identify the strategies you used to answer them on the lines below the questions.

1. What does the reader learn from Nya's introduction? (Select <u>two</u>.)

    A. how old she is

    B. the setting she is in

    C. the outcome of her journey

    D. how many siblings she has

    E. her family's relationship to the war

    Strategies:

    _____

    _____

    _____

    _____

2. What is the main feeling created by the description in Nya's section?

    A. difficulty

    B. enjoyment

    C. hope

    D. sadness

    Strategies:

    _____

    _____

    _____

    _____

3. How does the author create surprise in Salva's section of this chapter?

    A. by showing the conflict between Salva and the teacher

    B. by explaining why Salva enjoys playing with his brothers

    C. by showing how Salva learned the lesson in school already

    D. by contrasting a calm setting with the loud sound of gunshots

    Strategies:

    _____

    _____

    _____

    _____

4. What does the ending of the chapter suggest about Salva?

    A. that he is used to conflict

    B. that he will soon find safety

    C. that he is leaving behind what he knows

    D. that he is preparing to fight against the rebels

    Strategies:

    _____

    _____

    _____

    _____

Homework: Text-Dependent Questions:
A Long Walk to Water, Chapter 3

Name: _____ **Date:**_____

Part I

Directions: Reread each passage from chapter 3 of *A Long Walk to Water*. Then answer the questions below each passage.

1. "The dirt under her feet turned to mud, then **sludge**, until at last she was ankle-deep in water." (14)

    What word in this sentence <u>best</u> helps in understanding the meaning of **sludge**? (L.7.4a, L.7.6)

    A. dirt

    B. feet

    C. mud

    D. water

2. **Part A**

    "It took two **gourdfuls** before she felt a little cooler inside." (14)

    Complete the chart below to break up the word **gourdfuls** into a suffix and root. You may use your affix list as a resource. (L.7.4b)

gourdfuls	Root: gourd	Suffix:
Meaning	the rounded fruit of a plant related to the squash	

Part B

Use what you know about these word parts to write a definition of **gourdfuls** in your own words. (L.7.4b, L.7.6)

_____

_____

_____

3. "The woman looked up and saw him. Salva **flinched** at her glance." (16)

Write a first guess of what you think the word **flinched** means in this context.

_____

_____

_____

Use a print or online dictionary. Below, copy the meaning of the word **flinched** as it is used in this sentence. (L.7.4c, L.7.4d, L.7.6)

_____

_____

_____

4. "Squatting on his **haunches** next to her, Salva shelled the nuts and ate them." (17)

Write a first guess of what you think the word **haunches** means in this context:

_____

_____

_____

Use a print or online dictionary. Below, copy the meaning of the word **haunches** as it is used in this sentence. (L.7.4c, L.7.4d, L.7.6)

_____

_____

_____

Part II

Directions: Use the text to answer these questions about how the setting shapes the characters and plot and how Linda Sue Park develops and contrast different points of the view in chapter 3 of *A Long Walk to Water*.

5. Review Salva's narrative beginning on page 15. What is the setting? Describe the time and place. How does the setting shape Salva and what happens to him? What kind of person does Salva have to be in this setting? Use text evidence to support your response. (RL.7.3)

_____

_____

_____

_____

_____

_____

_____

_____

_____

_____

All quotations in this handout from:
Park, Linda Sue. *A Long Walk to Water: Based on a True Story*. Houghton Mifflin Harcourt, 2010. Chapter 3.

Homework: Analyze Point of View:
A Long Walk to Water, Chapter 4

Name: _____ **Date:** _____

Directions: Complete the chart to show Nya's point of view of taking her little sister with her (page 20) and Salva's point of view of what the Dinka people think of him (page 21).

Tip:

What is something that is similar about these two experiences? For example, what is similar about how other people see Salva and Nya's little sister?

Nya	Salva
How do you know? How has the author developed this point of view?	How do you know? How has the author developed this point of view?

Homework: Themes and Summary: *A Long Walk to Water*, Chapter 7

Name: _____ **Date:** _____

Directions: An author can use characters, descriptions, and other tools to develop the theme in a chapter. Use the text to answer the questions below about how the author develops a theme in chapter 7 of *A Long Walk to Water*.

1. Read this sentence from chapter 7:

   "If it hadn't been for Uncle, Salva might have gone crazy with fear" (41).

   What theme in the text does this sentence help develop?

   A. Nature can present many challenges to humans.

   B. Dangerous situations can make people become leaders.

   C. People need to depend on one another in order to survive.

   D. People often do not appreciate what they have until it is gone.

2. How are Nya's and Salva's uncles similar in this chapter? How does this develop the theme you identified in question 1?

   _____

   _____

   _____

   _____

   _____

   _____

   _____

   _____

   _____

3. How does the boat-building scene further develop the theme you identified above? Use examples from the text to support your answer.

_____

_____

_____

_____

_____

_____

_____

4. (Thinking about Thinking) How are writing summaries and discussing themes in a text similar? How are they different? Use the example of the boat-building scene to think of this difference. If you were summarizing the scene, what would you write? What would you say if you were talking about the theme?

_____

_____

_____

_____

_____

_____

_____

_____

Homework: Summary and Theme: *A Long Walk to Water*, Chapter 8

Name: _____ **Date:**_____

Directions: Answer the following questions to help you analyze the theme of chapter 8.

1. What does the author mean when she writes that Akeer's laugh "was like music" (45)?

    A. It was loud.

    B. It made Nya happy.

    C. It went on for a long time.

    D. It sounded strange to Nya.

2. Describe the way Nya's mood changes over the course of her section. Use evidence from the text.

    _____

    _____

    _____

    _____

    _____

    _____

    _____

    _____

    _____

    _____

    _____

3. How do the words **abundance** and **impressive** contribute to understanding Salva's feelings as he arrives at the island of fishermen on page 47?

    A. They show that he is jealous about where the fishermen live.

    B. They show why he wants to leave the group and join the fishermen.

    C. They show how excited he is to see all the food the fishermen have.

    D. They show that he is uncertain about whether the fishermen will help.

Homework: Text-Dependent Questions: *A Long Walk to Water*, Chapter 10

Name: _____ **Date:_____**

Directions: Answer the following questions to help you discuss theme in chapter 10 of *A Long Walk to Water*.

1. Reread these sentences:

   "Salva reached for his gourd. He knew it to be half full, but suddenly it felt much lighter, as if there was hardly any water left in it" (58).

   What does this description say about the water in the gourd?

   A. Salva is just realizing he is carrying the wrong water gourd.

   B. Carrying the water for so long is making some of it evaporate.

   C. Salva is mistaken about how much water was left in the gourd.

   D. The idea of having to give away water makes it seem like there's less of it.

2. Reread this sentence:

   "Like a miracle, the small amounts of water revived them. They were able to stagger to their feet and join the group as the walking continued" (58).

   Based on context, what is the meaning of **revived** as it is used in this sentence?

   A. caused to be tired

   B. made more visible

   C. brought back to life

   D. affected in a strong way

3. Reread the text from page 59:

    "If he were older and stronger, would he have given water to those men? Or would he, like most of the group, have kept his water for himself?"

    What do these questions show about Salva in this part of the story? How does this develop the theme?

    _____

    _____

    _____

    _____

    _____

4. Look more closely at the ways Salva's thinking and state of mind are described in the text with these examples:

    "He felt sick at the thought of those men" (59).

    ". . . a worry that had been growing like a long shadow across his thoughts . . ." (59)

    "Salva shook his head, unable to imagine what life would be like in the camp without Uncle" (60).

    "I mustn't act like a baby—I must try to be strong" (60).

    How do these descriptions of Salva's thinking develop a theme in the text? Use evidence from these quotes or other quotes in the book in your response.

    _____

    _____

    _____

    _____

    _____

    _____

5. Reread this sentence:

   "'Maybe they will leave us alone now that they have robbed us,' Salva thought" (63).

   How does this sentence affect the ending of the chapter?

   _____

   _____

   _____

   _____

   _____

6. Write a brief, objective summary of chapter 10, following the criteria you established in earlier lessons.

   _____

   _____

   _____

   _____

   _____

   _____

   _____

   _____

   _____

All quotations in this handout from:
Park, Linda Sue. *A Long Walk to Water: Based on a True Story*. Houghton Mifflin Harcourt, 2010. Chapter 10.

Unit 2: Write to Inform: The Lost Children of South Sudan

Common Core State Standards addressed:

- RL.7.1, RL.7.9
- RI.7.1, RI.7.2
- W.7.2, W.7.2a, W.7.2b, W.7.2c, W.7.2d, W.7.2e, W.7.2f, W.7.4, W.7.6, W.7.7, W.7.8, W.7.9a, W.7.9b
- SL.7.2

 Guiding Questions and Big Ideas

Who are The Lost Boys of the Sudan, and what is their story?

- *The second Sudanese civil war displaced millions of people, including hundreds of thousands of Lost Boys who walked through southern Sudan, Ethiopia, and Kenya in search of a safe haven.*

What are the habits of character the Lost Boys used to survive?

- *The Lost Children persevered to overcome the hardships of war, starvation, thirst, displacement, and threats by wild animals. Many of them show respect, empathy, and integrity as they help each other survive these same hardships. Some of them have also become leaders in the United States or in their home country (like Salva and his organization Water for South Sudan), using their strengths to help others grow, helping care for their environment and shared spaces, and using their learning to do so.*

- *In Sudan there are water scarcity issues, which means many people do not have easy access to clean water. As a result, most girls and women persevere to walk all day to get water. They also show empathy and respect as they care for others as many people get sick from the only water available, dirty water.*

What will your student be doing at school?

Students begin the unit researching to answer the questions generated while reading *A Long Walk to Water* during Unit 1, including questions about Lost Girls too. While researching, they determine two or more central ideas in informational texts and provide objective summaries of them. Students also watch clips of the documentary *God Grew Tired of Us* about The Lost Boys of the Sudan, analyzing the main ideas and supporting details and explaining how the ideas clarify what they have been researching. In the second half of the unit, students use the Painted Essay® structure to write an informative essay comparing and contrasting how the novel and an informational text deal with the subject matter of the Lost Children of Sudan.

Central to the EL Education curriculum is a focus on "habits of character" and social-emotional learning. Students work to become effective learners, developing mindsets and skills for success in college, career, and life (e.g., initiative, responsibility, perseverance, and collaboration); work to become ethical people, treating others well and standing up for what is right (e.g., empathy, integrity, respect, and compassion); and work to contribute to a better world, putting their learning to use to improve communities (e.g., citizenship and service).

In this unit, students focus on the habits of character of respect, empathy, and compassion as they respond to one another's ideas and skills in written work and in discussions. Also, students focus on integrity and perseverance as they work independently on assessments. Then as they track progress on their assessments, they take responsibility for their own learning.

How can you support your student at home?

Talk with your student about the Lost Boys and Girls of Sudan or other children/people displaced from their homes by war or disasters.

Read books or articles and watch documentaries with your student and summarize the chapters or scenes, noting the themes or central ideas, the message the author/director is conveying. One documentary you can watch with your student is *God Grew Tired of Us*, available online for free streaming. Students watch several short clips from this documentary and may enjoy and benefit from watching the whole film. Also, discuss with your student the research he/she is doing to answer questions about the Lost Children of Sudan. You may use questions such as the following for your conversations:

■ What are the main points of this chapter/book/article/documentary? What message is the author/directory trying to send?

■ What questions do you have about the Lost Children of Sudan? How are you answering those questions? How do you know your sources are credible (trustworthy)? Does this source answer your question? If so, how? If not, what will you do to try to answer the question?

Unit 2: Homework

In Lessons 1, 4, 7, and 14 students read chapters of *A Long Walk to Water* to prepare for in-class reading and discussion of the chapters.

In Lessons 1 and 2, students answer selected response (multiple choice) questions about the plot (or events) happening in chapter 1 of *A Long Walk to Water* or the documentary *God Grew Tired of Us*.

In Lessons 2–3, 5–6, and 8–13, homework focuses on research reading for which students read a topic-related book of choice and answer a question related to the unit's ideas and skills.

Research Reading: When not reading their anchor text, your student is expected to independently research the topic by reading topic-related books of his or her choice for approximately 20 minutes each day and responding to a prompt of choice in the front of the independent reading journal. These are usually books your student will bring home from school; however, they may be topic-related books chosen by the student at the public or your home library. Prompts for independent reading can be found in the homework materials provided below.

In Lessons 3–4, students work on their researching skills, refining their research questions and revising a summary of one of their sources.

In Lesson 9, students revise their focus statements for their end of unit assessments, making sure they are clear and include at least two main points.

Lesson	Lesson Content	Homework Practice	Due In	Anticipated Date[1]
1	Students participate in a close reading and Language Dive of "The 'Lost Girls' of Sudan," focusing on identifying main ideas and details in order to write a summary of the article.	1. Students complete Homework: Main Idea and Details: "The 'Lost Girls' of Sudan" to scaffold their understanding about main ideas and details and to prepare for similar questions on the mid-unit assessment. 2. Students read chapter 13 of *A Long Walk to Water* to prepare for in-class reading and discussion of the chapter.	Lesson 2	
2	Students continue to read *A Long Walk to Water* as well as broaden their understanding of the context for the events in the novel by watching and analyzing a clip of the video *God Grew Tired of Us*.	1. Students read for at least 20 minutes in their independent research reading text. Then they select a prompt and write a response in their independent reading journal. 2. Students complete Homework: Main Idea and Details: *God Grew Tired of Us* (11:07–13:30) to scaffold their understanding about main ideas and details and to prepare for similar questions on the mid-unit assessment.	Lesson 3	
3	Students learn or review the steps for conducting research on a topic, including refining a research question, evaluating sources, gathering information, and sharing their research questions and information gathered with a partner.	1. As necessary, students complete Homework: Continue Refining Questions to continue refining their research questions based on the research they conducted. 2. Students read for at least 20 minutes in their independent research reading text. Then they select a prompt and write a response in their independent reading journal.	Lesson 4	

[1] Teacher note: Please complete the Anticipated Date column according to your schedule.

Lesson	Lesson Content	Homework Practice	Due In	Anticipated Date[1]
4	Students continue researching to answer their questions about The Lost Boys of the Sudan. Students also write a summary of one of their sources.	1. Using the lessons learned from the whole-group summary critique activity, students complete Homework: Revise Summary to revise their own summaries. 2. Students read chapter 14 of *A Long Walk to Water* to prepare for in-class reading and discussion of the chapter.	Lesson 5	
5–6	Students continue to read *A Long Walk to Water* and demonstrate their skills in researching and answering questions related to the text. Students complete Part I of the mid-unit assessment as they watch a clip of *God Grew Tired of Us* and answer selected response questions related to the main ideas and supporting details in the video clip. Then students complete Part II of their mid-unit assessment as they research online to answer a question about *A Long Walk to Water*.	1. Students read for at least 20 minutes in their independent research reading text. Then they select a prompt and write a response in their independent reading journal.	Lesson 7	
7	Students analyze a model informative essay to identify the gist and the author's purpose of the essay. Then students explore the Painted Essay® structure to generate criteria for their own essays.	1. Students read chapter 15 of *A Long Walk to Water* to prepare for in-class reading and discussion of the chapter.	Lesson 8	
8	Students read chapter 15 of *A Long Walk to Water* and reread and analyze the article "The 'Lost Girls' of Sudan" to compare and contrast events in the article and events in the novel in preparation for their end of unit assessment.	1. Students read for at least 20 minutes in their independent research reading text. Then they select a prompt and write a response in their independent reading journal.	Lesson 9	

Lesson	Lesson Content	Homework Practice	Due In	Anticipated Date[1]
9	Students continue to compare and contrast *A Long Walk to Water* and the article "The 'Lost Girls' of Sudan." Students also participate in a Language Dive and plan the introductory paragraph for their compare and contrast essay.	1. Students complete Homework: Focus Statements to review and revise their focus statements and to ensure they are answering the prompt. 2. Students read for at least 20 minutes in their independent research reading text. Then they select a prompt and write a response in their independent reading journal.	Lesson 10	
10	Students plan the proof paragraphs for their compare and contrast essays, identifying their main points, gathering and organizing evidence to support these points, and explaining how the evidence supports their points.	1. Students read for at least 20 minutes in their independent research reading text. Then they select a prompt and write a response in their independent reading journal.	Lesson 11	
11	Students participate in a Language Dive and plan the conclusion paragraph of their essays, including a reflection.	1. Students read for at least 20 minutes in their independent research reading text. Then they select a prompt and write a response in their independent reading journal.	Lesson 12	
12–13	Students complete their End of Unit 2 Assessments, in which they write the essays they've been planning over the previous several lessons. Students draw on evidence to compare and contrast the novel *A Long Walk to Water* and the informational article "The 'Lost Girls' of Sudan" to analyze how the author of the novel uses or alters history.	1. Students read for at least 20 minutes in their independent research reading text. Then they select a prompt and write a response in their independent reading journal.	Lesson 13	
14	Students participate in a Language Dive on transitions, then provide feedback to partners on their informative essays and incorporate the feedback as they revise their essays.	1. Students read chapter 16 of *A Long Walk to Water* to prepare for in-class reading and discussion of the chapter.	Unit 3, Lesson 1	

Independent Reading

Directions: Remember to record responses to research reading in the front of your independent reading journal and responses to choice reading in the back. Try to choose a different prompt each time. Record any new vocabulary in your vocabulary log. Underline vocabulary found during independent reading.

Record:

- Date
- Title and author of your reading book
- Pages you have read
- Prompt
- Response

Example:

Date: 09/25/20

Book Title and Author: *A Long Walk to Water* by Linda Sue Park

Pages Read: 51–75

Prompt: How does the setting affect (character/person)? What kind of person does he/she have to be in that setting?

Response: The setting of the desert affects Salva by challenging him almost beyond his limits. He feels he cannot go on, but his uncle tells him to just walk "one painful step at a time" (54). Salva survives the desert with this help from his uncle. This setting makes Salva severely challenged and forces him to be strong, persevere, and rely on the support of others.

Consider using the following independent reading prompts.[2]

- How does this text add to your understanding of one of the guiding questions of the module?

- How does the setting affect (character/person)? What kind of person does he/she have to be in that setting?

- What kind of events does (character/person) experience in the setting?

- From whose point of view is this part of the text told? How does the author develop this person's/character's point of view?

- How does reading from the author's/character's point of view help you understand something about Sudan?

- What theme or central idea is present in the text you read? Give text details that convey that theme or central idea.

- How does (character/person)'s experiences relate to Salva's?

- How does (character/person)'s experiences relate to Nya's?

- How does (character/person) grow and change?

- If you were (character/person), what would you do differently?

- Record two or three facts in your own words that you learned from the text.

- Summarize your research reading today in no more than five sentences.

- What questions do you have about the topic after reading?

- Choose one new word from your reading today and analyze it on a vocabulary square.

[2] Some of the prompts will not be appropriate for the text students are reading. Invite students to choose a prompt that works for the text they have just read.

Definition in your own words	Synonyms (words with the same meaning)
Words with the same affix or root	**Sketch**

Translation in home language (if appropriate)

Vocabulary

Directions: In the classroom, you have been recording words from your texts in your vocabulary log. Throughout this unit, you have been research reading topic-related books at home to build your knowledge of Sudan and recording words in your independent reading journal.

Choose a word from your research reading or from a text you've read in class and add the word to your vocabulary log. Try to choose a different word to add and to practice a different vocabulary strategy each time. For each word, be sure to add the following:

1. The definition, or meaning, of the word

2. The vocabulary strategy you used to figure out the meaning of the word

3. A sketch or diagram that helps you to better understand the meaning of the word

Record new vocabulary in vocabulary logs and mark academic vocabulary with a symbol, for example a star:

- Academic vocabulary: words you might find in informational texts on many different topics. For example, the words evidence and rationale are words that could be found in books on any topic.

- Domain-specific vocabulary: words about a particular topic. For example, the words tadpoles, frogspawn, and amphibian are some that would be found on the topic of frogs.

Vocabulary Strategies

As a reminder, the vocabulary strategies we've been working on in class are:

- Context: Read the sentence around the word.

- Look at the affixes for clues.

- Look at the root of the word for clues.

- Use a dictionary.

- Discuss the word with another person (after attempting some of the above strategies).

Homework: Main Idea and Details: "The 'Lost Girls' of Sudan"

Name: _____ **Date:**_____

1. **Part A**

   Which of the following are the main ideas in this article? Select all that apply. (RI.7.2)

   A. The Lost Girls' human rights have been violated.

   B. Most Lost Girls work like unpaid servants.

   C. The Lost Boys and the Lost Girls have been treated differently.

   D. The Lost Boys lived in villages in the camp while the Lost Girls were placed in families.

   Part B

   Which supporting details from the video clip best support the main ideas identified in Part A? Select all that apply. (RI.7.2)

   A. The girls and boys walked hundreds of miles and faced many dangers to reach the camps.

   B. The girls are at risk of being married off against their wishes.

   C. The boys were kept in a group while the girls were separated.

   D. Three thousand girls arrived at the camp.

2. Which of the following questions does this article answer? (RI.7.2)

   A. What happened to the boys who didn't go to the United States?

   B. How can we help the Lost Girls of Sudan?

   C. Why were the girls treated differently from the boys?

   D. What happened to the girls who arrived at the refugee camp alone?

Homework: Main Idea and Details: *God Grew Tired of Us* (11:07–13:30)

Name: _____ **Date:**_____

Directions: If possible, view the video clip before answering these questions. If not, use your Main Idea and Details note-catcher from Lesson 2 to answer the following questions.

1. **Part A**

   Which of the following are the main ideas in this video clip? Select all that apply. (SL.7.2)

   A. Sometimes there wasn't enough food in the camp.

   B. For some, the journey was easier than life in the camp.

   C. The boys were safer in the new camp, but life was still difficult.

   D. The boys had good food and education at the camp.

   Part B

   Which supporting details from the video clip best support the main ideas identified in Part A? Select all that apply. (SL.7.2)

   A. People fight over food in the camp.

   B. The camp schools have lots of supplies.

   C. One girl describes how happy she was to make it to the camp.

   D. One boy talks about his difficulties at the camp.

2. Which of the following questions does this clip answer? (SL.7.2)

   A. What happened to the girls in Sudan?

   B. What was life like in the camp?

   C. Why were the people of Sudan fighting?

   D. What kinds of work could the boys do at the camp?

Homework: Continue Refining Questions

Name: _____ **Date:**_____

Directions: As necessary, continue refining your research questions based on the research you conducted today. Below, record each of your research questions and your thoughts about how they must change based on your research. Then revise the questions that need revising.

Research Questions and Thoughts about How They Should Change

_____

_____

_____

_____

_____

_____

Revised Research Questions

_____

_____

_____

_____

_____

_____

Homework: Revise Summary

Name: _____ **Date:**_____

Directions: Use the lessons learned from the whole-group summary critique activity to revise your own summary of a source you read in class today. Record your revised summary below.

_____

_____

_____

_____

_____

_____

_____

_____

_____

_____

_____

_____

Homework: Focus Statements

Name: _____ **Date:**_____

Directions: Review and revise your focus statement for your End of Unit 3 Compare and Contrast Essay. Make sure the focus statement is clear, includes at least two main points, and answers the prompt (see below). Record your revised focus statement below.

End of Unit 3 Assessment Prompt: How has the author of *A Long Walk to Water* used or altered history in the novel? In this essay, you will compare and contrast *A Long Walk to Water* with the informational text "The 'Lost Girls' of Sudan."

_____

_____

_____

_____

_____

_____

_____

_____

_____

_____

_____

_____

_____

_____

Unit 3: Write to Raise Awareness: The Lost Children of South Sudan

Common Core State Standards addressed:

- RL.7.1, RL.7.7

- W.7.3, W.7.3a, W.7.3b, W.7.3c, W.7.3e, W.7.4, W.7.6, W.7.10

 Guiding Questions and Big Ideas

Who are the Lost Boys of Sudan, and what is their story?

- *The second Sudanese civil war displaced millions of people, including hundreds of thousands of Lost Boys who walked through southern Sudan, Ethiopia, and Kenya in search of a safe haven.*

What are the habits of character the Lost Boys used to survive?

- *The Lost Children persevered to overcome the hardships of war, starvation, thirst, displacement, and threats by wild animals. Many of them show respect, empathy, and integrity as they help each other survive these same hardships. Some of them have also become leaders in the United States or in their home country (like Salva and his organization Water for South Sudan), using their strengths to help others grow, helping care for their environment and shared spaces, and using their learning to do so.*

- *In Sudan there are water scarcity issues, which means many people do not have easy access to clean water. As a result, most girls and women persevere to walk all day to get water. They also show empathy and respect as they care for others as many people get sick from the only water available, dirty water.*

What will your student be doing at school?

Students will begin Unit 3 comparing *A Long Walk to Water* to the audiobook version of the text, exploring how authors and readers develop tone, mood, and expression. Students will draw on this exploration as they start the second half of the unit, planning and then writing a narrative children's book about a Lost Boy or Girl of Sudan. Through mini lessons and independent planning work, students focus on developing characters, settings, plot points, and narrative techniques such as pacing, description, and dialogue. Once students complete a draft of their narrative, they convert it into an ebook and publish it by sharing it with others, especially elementary school children.

Central to the EL Education curriculum is a focus on "habits of character" and social-emotional learning. Students work to become effective learners, developing mindsets and skills for success in college, career, and life (e.g., initiative, responsibility, perseverance, and collaboration); work to become ethical people, treating others well and standing up for what is right (e.g., empathy, integrity, respect, and compassion); and work to contribute to a better world, putting their learning to use to improve communities (e.g., citizenship and service).

In this unit, students focus on respect, empathy, and compassion habits of character as they respond to each other's ideas and skills in written work and in discussions. Also, students focus on integrity and perseverance as they work independently on assessments. Then as they track progress on their assessments, they take responsibility for their own learning. Finally, as students develop an ebook about a Lost Boy or Girl of Sudan, they help others in the class grow as they assist with technology and writing. Also, because students will share their ebooks with an elementary school child in their community, they focus on using their learning to improve their community.

How can you support your student at home?

Talk with your student about the Lost Boys and Girls of Sudan or other children/people displaced from their homes by war or disasters.

Discuss with your student about the habits of character that the Lost Boys and Girls or other children/people need in order to survive hardships.

Talk with your student about the habits of character that the Lost Boys or other children/people need in order to be successful in a new country.

Read and listen to stories (audiobooks are available at the library), discussing how the audio is different from the text and how the audio uses sounds, tones of voice, and other techniques to make meaning.

Unit 3: Homework

Throughout the unit, homework focuses on research reading and determining the meaning of unfamiliar words using context and reference materials.

Research Reading: When not reading their anchor text, your student is expected to independently research the topic by reading topic-related books of his or her choice for approximately 20 minutes each day and responding to a prompt of choice in the front of the independent reading journal. These are usually books your student will bring home from school; however, they may be topic related books chosen by the student at the public or home library. Prompts for independent reading can be found in the homework materials provided below.

Create Illustrations: Additional homework beginning in Lesson 4 involves students creating illustrations for the narrative children's book they are writing. Students will create these illustrations either in art class or at home and materials (art supplies) will be provided as necessary. Students can use any medium to create the illustrations (paint, marker, crayon, colored pencil, torn paper, photographs, etc.)

Lesson	Lesson Content	Homework Practice	Due In	Anticipated Date[1]
1	Students continue reading the novel *A Long Walk to Water* (chapter 16) and listen to an audio version of the book to compare and contrast the effects of each medium. Students conclude the lesson by sharing their ideas on how the audio compares to text.	1. Students read chapter 17 of *A Long Walk to Water* to prepare for in-class reading and discussion of the chapter.	Lesson 2	
2	Students continue reading the novel *A Long Walk to Water* and listen to an audio version of the book to compare and contrast the effects of each medium. Students also participate in a Language Dive, exploring the deeper meaning and structures of a sentence in chapter 17 of both the textual and the audio version of the novel.	1. Students read for at least 20 minutes in their independent research reading text. Then they select a prompt and write a response in their independent reading journal.	Lesson 3	
3	Students compare an excerpt from the audio version of *A Long Walk to Water* with an excerpt of the text from chapter 1, comparing the effects of the techniques in the versions. Students focus on working to become effective learners and ethical people by reading and answering questions independently with perseverance and integrity for the mid-unit assessment.	1. Students read chapter 18 of *A Long Walk to Water* to prepare for in-class reading and discussion of the chapter.	Lesson 4	
4	Students read chapter 18 of *A Long Walk to Water*, the concluding chapter of the novel. Students then analyze the narrative children's book *Nasreen's Secret School* in order to determine the criteria for writing their own stories about a Lost Boy or Girl of Sudan.	1. In art class or at home, students follow the instructions on Homework: Create Illustrations to begin creating illustrations for their narrative children's ebook. 2. Students read the "Message from Salva" and author's note sections of *A Long Walk to Water* to prepare for in-class reading and discussion of these sections.	Lesson 5 Lesson 10	

[1] Teacher note: Please complete the Anticipated Date column according to your schedule.

Lesson	Lesson Content	Homework Practice	Due In	Anticipated Date[1]
5	Students finish reading *A Long Walk to Water* by analyzing the author's note. Then students use the model narrative *Nasreen's Secret School* to plan the character and settings of their own narratives about a Lost Child of Sudan. Students conclude the lesson by sharing their plans with a partner to get feedback and orally rehearse their ideas which can help with further planning.	1. Students read for at least 20 minutes in their independent research reading text. Then they select a prompt and write a response in their independent reading journal.	Lesson 6	
		2. In art class or at home, students follow the instructions on Homework: Create Illustrations to begin creating illustrations for their narrative children's ebook.	Lesson 10	
		3. Students think of a plot for their stories, which they will develop in the next lesson.	Lesson 6	
6	Students use the model narrative and their notes and research related to *A Long Walk to Water* to plan the plot of their own narratives about a Lost Child of Sudan. Students also participate in a Language Dive focusing on the meaning of figurative language in *Nasreen's Secret School* and how the sentence is part of an effective narrative conclusion. Students conclude the lesson by sharing their plans with a partner to get feedback and orally rehearse their ideas, which can help with further planning.	1. Students read for at least 20 minutes in their independent research reading text. Then they select a prompt and write a response in their independent reading journal.	Lesson 7	
		2. In art class or at home, students follow the instructions on Homework: Create Illustrations to begin creating illustrations for their narrative children's ebook.	Lesson 10	

Lesson	Lesson Content	Homework Practice	Due In	Anticipated Date[1]
7	Students learn about how description and dialogue can impact pacing. Then students apply this learning to plan the pacing, dialogue, and description of their narrative about a Lost Child of Sudan.	1. Students read for at least 20 minutes in their independent research reading text. Then they select a prompt and write a response in their independent reading journal.	Lesson 8	
		2. Students add transitions from their Narrative Transition Words and Phrases handout to the pacing table in their Narrative Writing Plan graphic organizers.	Lesson 8	
		3. In art class or at home, students follow the instructions on Homework: Create Illustrations to begin creating illustrations for their narrative children's ebook.	Lesson 10	
8	Students complete their End of Unit 3 Assessments, in which they write the narratives they've been planning over the previous several lessons. Students draw on their Narrative Writing Plan graphic organizers and the evidence they've collected throughout the module from *A Long Walk to Water* and related texts to draft a narrative that showcases the habits of character that a Lost Boy or Girl of Sudan demonstrated in his/her journeys.	1. Students read for at least 20 minutes in their independent research reading text. Then they select a prompt and write a response in their independent reading journal.	Lesson 9	
		2. In art class or at home, students follow the instructions on Homework: Create Illustrations to begin creating illustrations for their narrative children's ebook.	Lesson 10	

Lesson	Lesson Content	Homework Practice	Due In	Anticipated Date[1]
9	Students review the performance task assignment and anchor chart to generate criteria of an effective performance task. Students also review the author's notes from *A Long Walk to Water* and *Nasreen's Secret School* to use them as models for the author's note to their ebooks. Then students write their author's note for their ebook. Students conclude the lesson by sharing their work with the class, noting successes and challenges with technology and with writing the author's note.	1. Students read for at least 20 minutes in their independent research reading text. Then they select a prompt and write a response in their independent reading journal. 2. In art class or at home, students follow the instructions on Homework: Create Illustrations to complete the illustrations for their narrative children's ebook.	Lesson 10 Lesson 10	
10–11	Students use technology to create their ebook of their narrative about a Lost Child of Sudan. Then students share their work with a partner, noting successes and challenges with technology.	1. None.		

Independent Reading

Directions: Remember to record responses to research reading in the front of your independent reading journal and responses to choice reading in the back. Try to choose a different prompt each time. Record any new vocabulary in your vocabulary log. Underline vocabulary found during independent reading.

Record:

- Date
- Title and author of your reading book
- Pages you have read
- Prompt
- Response

Example:

<u>Date:</u> 10/15/2020

<u>Book Title and Author:</u> *A Long Walk to Water* by Linda Sue Park

<u>Pages Read:</u> 97–121

<u>Prompt:</u> Which habits of character are demonstrated in the text? Explain.

<u>Response:</u> Salva shows perseverance by not giving up learning English, adapting to the very different life in the United States, and working through all the problems of working on his project. Salva also demonstrates empathy, compassion, and improving his community by returning to Sudan and bringing people water.

Consider using the following independent reading prompts.[2]

- How does this text add to your understanding of one of the Guiding Questions of the Module?

- If you listened to audio or watched video, what techniques were used and how did these techniques create meaning?

- Which habits of character are demonstrated in the text? Explain.

- How does (character/person)'s experiences relate to Salva's?

- How does (character/person)'s experiences relate to Nya's?

- How does (character/person) grow and change?

- If you were (character/person), what would you do differently?

- Record two or three facts in your own words that you learned from the text.

- Summarize your research reading today in no more than five sentences.

- What questions do you have about the topic after reading?

- Choose one new word from your reading today and analyze it on a vocabulary square:

[2] Some of the prompts will not be appropriate for the text students are reading. Invite students to choose a prompt that works for the text they have just read.

Definition in your own words	Synonyms (words with the same meaning)

Words with the same affix or root	Sketch

Translation in home language (if appropriate)

Vocabulary

Directions: In the classroom, you have been recording words from your texts in your vocabulary log. Throughout this unit, you have been research reading topic-related books at home to build your knowledge of the Lost Children of Sudan and recording words in your independent reading journal.

Choose a word from your research reading or from a text you've read in class and add the word to your vocabulary log. Try to choose a different word to add and to practice a different vocabulary strategy each time. For each word, be sure to add the following:

1. The definition, or meaning, of the word

2. The vocabulary strategy you used to figure out the meaning of the word

3. A sketch or diagram that helps you to better understand the meaning of the word

Record new vocabulary in vocabulary logs and mark academic vocabulary with a symbol, for example a star:

- Academic vocabulary: words you might find in informational texts on many different topics. For example, the words evidence and rationale are words that could be found in books on any topic.

- Domain-specific vocabulary: words about a particular topic. For example, the words tadpoles, frogspawn, and amphibian are some that would be found on the topic of frogs.

Vocabulary Strategies

As a reminder, the vocabulary strategies we've been working on in class are:

- Context: Read the sentence around the word.

- Look at the affixes for clues.

- Look at the root of the word for clues.

- Use a dictionary.

- Discuss the word with another person (after attempting some of the above strategies).

Homework: Create Illustrations

Name: _____ **Date:**_____

In class, you are planning your narrative to develop the character(s), settings, and plot. For homework, create illustrations that visually represent the character(s), settings, and main events of your story about a Lost Child of Sudan. You may use any medium or materials to create your illustrations (paint, marker, crayon, colored pencil, torn paper, photographs, etc.). (RL.7.7)

Homework: Add Transition Words

Name: _____ **Date:**_____

In class, you received and reviewed a handout on narrative transitions words. These words can be used to show the change from one time or space to another. Add transitions to your Narrative Writing Plan graphic organizer in the pacing section. These transitions are notes to remind you to use these transitions or similar ones when you draft your narrative in Lesson 8 for the End of Unit 3 Assessment. (W.7.3c)

Grade 7: Module 1

Affix List

Affix List

Name: _____ **Date:**_____

Prefixes (before the root)

Prefix	Definition	Examples	Origin
ad-	to, toward	adequate, adhere, adjective	Latin
com-, con-	with, together	commune, community, conjunction, combine, conspire, confluence	Latin
de-	off, from	deliver, deforest, dethrone, decamp	Latin
dia-	across, through	diabolical, diadem, diagnosis, diagonal, diagram, diameter	Greek
dis-	apart, away	displaced, disjointed, disoriented	Latin
epi-	on, upon, befall (happen to)	epidermis, epidemiology, epidemic	Greek
ex-, exo-	out of, from	exoskeleton, exterior, external	Greek
in-, im-, ir-, il-	not	inability, impatient, irregular, illegal	Latin
in-, im-	into, in, on, upon	inhabited, improve, informed	Latin
inter-	between	intercept, interview, interstate	Latin
micro-	small, minute	microbiology, microscope	Greek
pre-	before	predict, predate, preread	Latin
pro-	forward, forth, publicly	progress, proceed, produce	Latin
re-	again	research, reread, redo, regain	Latin
retro-	back, backward	retroactive, retrograde, retrospective	Latin
se-	apart	separate, select	Latin

Prefix	Definition	Examples	Origin
super-	above, on top of, beyond	superfine, superhuman, supersonic	Latin
syn-, sym-	with, together	sympathy, symphony, synthesis, synthetic, photosynthesis, synonym, synagogue, synchronize	Greek
trans-	across, change, through	transformation, transportation, transfer	Latin
un-	not	unfamiliar, unpopular, unlikely	Old English
uni-	one, single	unicorn, unicycle, uniform	Latin

Roots

Root	Definition	Examples	Origin
amo, amatum	love	amateur, amiable, amicable, amorous, enamored, enemy	Latin
aqua	water	aquarium, aqueduct, aquaculture, aquamarine	Latin
arbor, arboris	tree	arboretum, grape arbor, arborvitae	Latin
assess	to test	assess, assessment, assessor	Latin
aud	to hear	audible, audio, auditory	Latin
bene, boun, bon	good, well	benefit, benign, beneficial, Benedict, bonus, bonanza, bonbon, bounty	Latin
bonus	good	bonus, bonbon, bonny, bounty, bonanza, boon	Latin
chronos (chron)	time	chronological, synchronize, chronicle, chronic, chronometer	Greek
consist	adhering to the same principles	consistent, inconsistent, consists	Latin

Root	Definition	Examples	Origin
cred	believe	credible, credo, credence	Latin
dem(os)	people	democratic, epidemic, demographics	Greek
dendron	tree	rhododendron, dendrophile, dendrometer, dendriform	Greek
effectivus	practical	effect, effective, effectively	Latin
facio, factum, fy, fier	make, do	factory, manufacture, deface	Latin
familiaris	of a household	unfamiliar, familiar, family	Latin
figo, fixum	attach	fix, fixture, crucifix, affix, prefix, suffix	Latin
gen	create	generate, genesis, generator	Latin
habitare	dwell, live	inhabit, inhabited	Latin
hydros (hydr)	water	hydrogen, hydrant, hydroplane	Greek
identitas	same	identity, identical	Latin
ignis	fire	igneous, ignite, ignition	Latin
jungo, junctum	join	join, joint, conjunction, disjointed, junction, subjugate	Latin
kinesis, cinema	movement	kinetic, kinesiology, cinema, cinematographer	Greek
luna	moon	lunar, lunatic, lunacy, clair de lune, lunambulist, lunation	Latin
logos	word, speech	dialogue, monologue	Greek
magnus	large, big	magnify, magnifier, magnitude, magnificent, magnanimous	Latin
narr	to say, to tell	narrative, narrate, narrator	Latin

Root	Definition	Examples	Origin
occupare	to seize, take hold of, make one's own	occupy, preoccupied, occupation	Latin
philia, phile	love	philosopher, Philadelphia, philanthropist, Francophile	Greek
phobos	fear	phobia, claustrophobia, hydrophobia, phobophobia	Greek
platea	place, street, area	displaced, place, replace	Latin/Greek
pono, postum (pos, post)	put, place	pose, post, postage, position, deposit, depose, impose, component	Latin
port	to carry	portable, transport, export, portfolio, porter	Latin
scio, scitum (sci)	know	science, scientific, conscience, prescience, omniscience	Latin
scribe (scrib), scriptum (script)	to write	describe, manuscript, scriptures, inscribe, prescription, script	Latin
sonus	sound	sound, sonic, sonnet, sonovox, sonar, sonata, consonant	Latin
spectro, spect, spec	to see, watch, observe	spectate	Latin
tech	art and craft	techniques, technology	Greek
tempus, temporis	time	temporal, temporary, extemporaneous, contemporary, tempo	Latin

Root	Definition	Examples	Origin
testis, testari, testor	assert (to state with force or confidence), witness	protest, attest, testify	Latin
thermos (therm)	heat	thermometer, thermostat, thermos, thermal	Greek
vac	empty	vacate, evacuate, vacancy, vacuum, vacuous	Latin
verbum	word	verb, proverb, verbal, verbiage, verbose, verbatim, verbalize	Latin
vocare (voc, vok)	to call or summon	vocal, vocabulary, vocation, vocational, voice, revoke, invoke	Latin

Suffixes (after the root)

Suffix	Definition	Examples	Origin
-age	result of an action, collection	manage, drainage, acreage	Latin
-al	of or pertaining to; having the form of	identical, practical, natural	Latin
-cy, -cies	used to form an abstract noun	Inconsistency, inconsistencies, emergency, emergencies	Latin
-ed	past tense	jumped, pressed, pushed	Old English
-ent, -ant	an action, condition or causing a specific action	student, contestant, immigrant, obedient, absorbent, abundant, elegant	Latin
-ful	full of	gourdful, handful, fistful, helpful, careful	Old English
-hood	state, quality, condition of	neighborhood, childhood, brotherhood	Old English

Suffix	Definition	Examples	Origin
-ic	relating to, characterized by	energetic, historic	Latin/Greek
-ice	state or quality of	justice, service, accomplice, apprentice, injustice	Latin
-ify	to make, to form into	fortify, solidify, liquify	Latin
-ity, -ty	state of, quality of	prosperity, equality	Latin
-ish	like, having the characteristics of, inclined or tending to	childish, girlish, impish, freakish, bookish, oldish	Old English
-ist	person who practices or is concerned with	biologist, epidemiologist, florist	Latin/Greek
-ive	tending or having to do with	effective, objective, progressive, conservative	Latin
-ize	to make, to cause to become	fertilize, criticize, apologize	Latin/Greek
-less	without	tireless, childless, sleepless	Old English
-logy	study of	biology, epidemiology, geology	Latin/Greek
-ment	for nouns, showing action or state of being	assessment, refreshment, abridgment, ornament	Latin
-ous, -eous, -ious	full of, characterized by	adventurous, nervous, mysterious, courteous	Latin
-some	characterized by a thing, quality, state, or action	awesome, burdensome, winsome, quarrelsome	Old English
-ward	in the direction of	forward, toward, westward	Old English

Acknowledgments

Project management support, production design, and copyediting services provided by ScribeConcepts.com.

Notes

Notes

Notes

Notes